JO

Johnny Salter

A Play For Young People

by

Aidan Chambers

HEINEMANN EDUCATIONAL BOOKS
LONDON

Heinemann Educational Books Ltd
22 Bedford Square, London WC1B 3HA
LONDON EDINBURGH MELBOURNE AUCKLAND
HONG KONG SINGAPORE KUALA LUMPUR
NEW DELHI NAIROBI JOHANNESBURG IBADAN
EXETER(NH) KINGSTON PORT OF SPAIN

ISBN 0 435 23165 0

Cover photographs by David Long and
Alistair MacFarlane

Printed in Great Britain by
Richard Clay (The Chaucer Press) Ltd, Bungay, Suffolk

To the young people of
Archway School, Stroud

PRODUCTION NOTES

JOHNNY SALTER was written for the young people of Archway School, Stroud, who do a fair amount of spontaneous drama work. I tried to leave scope for the players themselves to create the characters in their own way and to work up scenes just as they work up their own short plays. The fights are obvious moments when this is intended to happen. The tea party scene is another. Thus, in scripting it for publication, though I have put in sufficient production detail to suggest the general lines and the mood of the scene, I hope that other producers and young players will disregard my suggestions when they feel they can perform it better in their own way. For this same reason, I had no wish to prepare a full acting edition.

The songs suggested in the script need not necessarily be the ones used. Specially written ones, or other commercial songs, more up to date than those scripted, or preferred by producer and players may be substituted.

In the original production, the 'adult' characters were costumed in the dress of sixty years ago, in order to make the point that young people often see adults as 'old', not of their time. Period costume also helps the young player to do that most difficult of all acting jobs – being a character older than oneself: it helps to emphasize in a valuable way the type of person the character is.

CHARACTERS

JOHNNY SALTER

SPARKLER BROWN

PUFF

NYLON

WRIGGLES

CARROTS

MR MOGGS, *nightwatchman*

1ST GIRL AND TWO COMPANIONS

BOUNCER BARTON

BIFF

SMIG

POLICEMAN

JOE

SALLY GRIMSHAW

HERBERT GRIMSHAW

MILLY GRIMSHAW

BELLA CHUNTER

COLONEL HECTOR CHUNTER

PENELOPE CHUNTER

ACT ONE

ACT TWO

ACT THREE

One Saturday in early autumn in a small industrial town.

ACT ONE

SCENE ONE

*The down-town housing estate of a small industrial town.
Walls. A lamp-post. Down left centre, a small dustbin. Early
autumn. Saturday morning.*

JOHNNY SALTER *sits very still against the Proscenium Arch,
looking into the audience.* SPARKLER BROWN *enters on
a bicycle which he stops skilfully by a wall. He glances at*
JOHNNY. *A pause.*

SPARKS: Hallo, Johnny.

JOHNNY: Hallo, Sparks. (*Pause.* JOHNNY *joins* SPARKS
by the wall.)

JOHNNY: What you gonna do?

SPARKS: Dunno. (*Pause.*)

JOHNNY: Don't like Saturday.

SPARKS: No.

JOHNNY: Don't like Saturday morning at all.

They climb the wall and sit on top, despondently. Pause.

SPARKS (*enthusiastically*): Bet I can spit farther than
you!

JOHNNY: Bet you can't!

SPARKS: Gob on that lamp-post then. (*They stand on the
wall.* JOHNNY *spits at the lamp-post.*)

SPARKS: Yar – missed!

JOHNNY: You try then.

SPARKS *spits at the lamp-post.*

JOHNNY: Missed!

SPARKS: Not as much as you.

JOHNNY: Weren't.

SPARKS: You arguing?

JOHNNY: Yes. What you going to do about it, then?

SPARKS *knocks* JOHNNY *off the wall and shouts:*

SPARKS: Half kill you! (*He jumps down on to* JOHNNY. *They fight and finish on the apron, ruffled and all smiles.*) *Pause.*

JOHNNY: Let's get the others.

SPARKS: O.K.

JOHNNY: Ready? One ... Two ... Three: (*They let out three high-pitched whistles. After a moment* PUFF *appears, struggling over the wall. He sits on top, puffing.*)

JOHNNY (*without looking at* PUFF): Hallo, Puff.

PUFF (*brightly*): Hallo, Johnny. Hallo, Sparks. I'm dead!

SPARKS: Suppose you've just got up?

PUFF: Yeah.

JOHNNY: And just eaten?

PUFF: Yea. How'd you guess?

JOHNNY: I wonder! (JOHNNY *goes to one side of* PUFF. SPARKS *returns to his bike.*)

PUFF: My Mum and Dad have gone to the races and left me my breakfast and dinner on the table so ...

SPARKS: ... So, don't tell me – you ate both at once?

PUFF: Yeah. How did you guess? Lovely! I had bacon sandwiches first. Cold of course, cos Mum done 'em before they went, see. And cornflakes, and ham what she left for my dinner, and cold peas from yesterday, and tin peaches, and milk, and ...

JOHNNY: Shut up, Puff, will you? You fatguts!

PUFF *belches loudly.*

PUFF: Excuse me. That's the pickles.

Enter NYLON *very dapper.*

NYLON: Hallo, you lot.

SPARKS and JOHNNY: Hallo, Nylon.

PUFF: Hallo, Nylon. I'm near dead.

NYLON: Near bursting, more likely.

Enter WRIGGLES.

JOHNNY: Hallo, Wriggles.

WRIGGLES: Hallo, Johnny. (*He sits down in the middle of them, quite at home and without more fuss.*) Just seen the 9.30 go through. Never seen a Jet-class diesel before. (*Pause. He looks round at the others.*) Johnny, what we going to do today?

JOHNNY: Dunno. You tell me.

WRIGGLES: I hate Saturday!

NYLON: Me, too. Used to like Saturdays. Used to be the best day of the week. No school. Up late. Muck about all day. But it's boring now somehow.

PUFF: Me, too. Used to be exciting. We used to do things. Why do we never do things now?

SPARKS: Like what, for instance?

PUFF: Well, I dunno . . . like playing commandos up the field. Yeah . . . let's have a game of commandos. (*He gives a hideous commando scream and dives at* NYLON *who pushes him away.* PUFF *falls.*)

NYLON: Mind my pullover! Don't know what my mother'll say!

PUFF: Well . . . it was only an idea.

NYLON: Then keep any similar brainy ideas locked up in that fat head of yours in future.

PUFF (*getting up*): Honest. You're just like my Dad, you

lot. He sits there in front of the telly on Saturday afternoons watching the wrestling and telling the blokes what can't hear anyhow, how bad they are. And if you move your little toe, he's on at you about finding something to do. (*He imitates his Dad.*) Can't understand it, a great lad like you. Ought to be out in the sunshine doing something. Not sitting around all day doing nothing but no good. (*Himself again.*) And all the time there he is goggling at the box.

A head comes up over the wall. It is CARROTS – *all tomboy and gawpy.*

CARROTS: Hallo, everybody!

They all look round and give a great moan.

CARROTS (*standing on the wall*): Thanks for the friendly welcome, boys.

JOHNNY: Look, Carrots, go home. We don't want you. How often do we have to tell you?

CARROTS: I know. Sad isn't it! (*She offers a bag of sweets.*) Have a liquorice.

JOHNNY: Now that's different!

Yelling in glee, they crowd round her and snaffle liquorice. WRIGGLES *can't reach.* JOHNNY *hauls him on to the wall between him and* CARROTS.

JOHNNY: Come on, Wriggles.

CARROTS: Well . . . thanks for the vote of confidence, boys.

SPARKS: Look, Carrots. We like you a lot. You know? It's nothing personal or anything. But we like your liquorice more. (*He takes one.*) May I? Thanks! But you know . . . this is a boy's gang and . . .

CARROTS: Don't tell me . . . I know (*jumping down*) girls is horrid. (*She sits on the dustbin.*)

SPARKS: That's it. (*He gets his bike and straddles it along-side* CARROTS.)

CARROTS: They are always on about clothes and boys and that sort of thing.

SPARKS: That's it.

CARROTS: They just moon about and giggle.

SPARKS: That's it. You've got it. You understand fine.

CARROTS: And you can't bear them.

SPARKS: You know, for a girl you're quite intelligent. You're all there. Can't stick them. So . . .

CARROTS: So neither can I. Have another liquorice.

PUFF (*passing behind them and taking a liquorice as he goes*): Me too! My Mum says girls is easier to bring up than boys. My Mum says she wished she had half a dozen girls rather than me.

NYLON: Knowing you, Puff, that doesn't surprise me!

CARROTS: My Mum says just the opposite.

SPARKS (*wryly*): And that doen't surprise me!

JOHNNY: Parents are pretty hopeless anyhow. The only reason you have them is so they can embarrass you. Look at my Dad. He does nothing but go to work, garden, go to the local, and watch telly. Do you know, I don't think I've ever had a sensible conversation with my Dad!

PUFF: That's just what I said about mine. Mine's just the same. It's not good enough. I think I'll start a Society for the Getting Rid of Parents.

NYLON (*sadly*): I ain't got a Dad.

SPARKS: Then you're lucky, Nylon. Honest.

WRIGGLES *has climbed the lamp-post as far as the ladder-bar. He is clinging on tightly.*

WRIGGLES: Johnny!

JOHNNY: Well, you're all right, Wriggles. Your Dad's all right.

WRIGGLES: I know . . . It's not that . . . It's . . .

JOHNNY: Well, there you are. You've nothing to worry about.

WRIGGLES: It's not that. It's . . .

JOHNNY: Well, what is it?

WRIGGLES: I'm stuck! I can't get down.

SPARKS: Oh, crikey, he's done it again. Come on, Johnny.

> SPARKS *jumps off his bike and pushes it at* NYLON *who catches it and places it against the wall.* JOHNNY, SPARKS *and* PUFF *gather round the lamp-post.* CARROTS *watches from the dustbin.*

PUFF: How often have we told you . . .

JOHNNY, SPARKS and PUFF: Don't climb things!

JOHNNY: You always get stuck.

WRIGGLES: I know. Get me down, Johnny.

JOHNNY: Come on. (*They build a human ladder up to* WRIGGLES. PUFF *is base,* then SPARKS, *then* JOHNNY.)

CARROTS: Be careful. If you drop him, he'll make a nasty hole in the pavement.

JOHNNY, SPARKS and NYLON (*in mock laughter*): Ha! Ha! (*They get* WRIGGLES *down. Enter* MOGGS, *the Nightwatchman.*)

MOGGS: Now then, what's going on?

ALL: Moggs! Mr Moggs! Good old, Moggy, etc., *ad lib.* (*They crowd round* MOGGS. WRIGGLES *jumps up and hangs round his neck.*)

PUFF: Where you going, Mr Moggs? Can we come with you?

WRIGGLES: Yes. We'll come with you.

MOGGS: Steady, boys, steady. I'm not going anywhere, really. Just into town to do some shopping, like. Nothing much. Just to get a bit of baccy, and then back up here to Joe's Place for me dinner, and me bait. (MOGGS *puts* WRIGGLES *down and sits on the dustbin. They gather round.*)

SPARKS: Well, we can come. We'd help.

MOGGS: You – help! No fear! Not in town on Saturday morning.

JOHNNY: Then can we take the dog out?

MOGGS: You leave my Jessie alone. She had her pups last night.

General rejoicing.

JOHNNY: How many, Mr Moggs?

MOGGS: Four. Three bitches and a dog.

NYLON: Can I have one, Mr Moggs?

MOGGS: You can that, son, when they're weaned, so long as your Mum says yes.

NYLON: Then that stops that! Last time I asked for one she said she wouldn't have one in the place. They only messed on the carpet, she said.

They all commiserate.

MOGGS: What you all hanging about the streets for? Haven't you nothing to do?

JOHNNY: No, it's Saturday and it's boring.

PUFF: Saturday is horrid.

WRIGGLES: Don't like Saturday.

MOGGS: Why don't you have a game?

JOHNNY: Games are kids stuff!

SPARKS: We ain't kids any more.

MOGGS (*smiling*): Oh. I see.

WRIGGLES: I dunno. I like games.

PUFF: But you're still a kid, Wriggles.

NYLON: Games ruffle up your clothes.

MOGGS: That so? Ah well. Must be off. (*He rises.*) Don't get up to any mischief, mind. Like last week when you tipped that dustbin all over that Barton boy.

JOHNNY: Over Bouncer? Well he deserved it.

SPARKS: Yes. He'd been asking for it all week. He's always bashing Wriggles or taking the mickey out of him.

JOHNNY: Yes. So we let him have it.

MOGGS: Ah well. Keep your noses clean. See you, boys! *All reply. Exit* MOGGS. *They re-group round the lamp-post.* CARROTS *sits on the wall, alone.* WRIGGLES *sits on the dustbin and looks at a train-spotting book.*

SPARKS: I like old Moggy.

JOHNNY: Yes, so do I. It must be a funny job being a nightwatchman.

SPARKS: Yes. Scare-making a bit. All them cases in that dark factory.

PUFF: Works at Grimshaw's don't he?

NYLON: Yes.

PUFF: My Dad says he's past it. He says that if anyone burgled the place the old man probably wouldn't be able to do much about it.

SPARKS: Then your Dad's a nut. Even if he is a bit old, I bet Moggy would beat any burglar.

JOHNNY: Yea, so do I. And anyway old Grimshaw isn't no idiot. He wouldn't have a nightwatchman that couldn't look after all the valuable stuff there must be in that warehouse.

PUFF: My Dad says there must be thousands of pounds worth of stuff in that building.

SPARKS: And for once, Puff, your Dad's probably right.
CARROTS (*pointing up the street with a look of horror*): Oo,
    I say, you chaps, Look! GIRLS! Ugh!

> CARROTS *dives behind the wall. The others yell in
> horror and follow her.* WRIGGLES *is left on the dustbin,
> bewildered at their sudden disappearance. As the girls enter
> he watches them with relish, waving coyly as they pass
> him.*

> *Enter* THREE SCHOOLGIRLS. *Two are listening with
> 'gone' faces as the third tells her story. They sigh romanti-
> cally from time to time.*

1ST. GIRL: Oh! It was terrific. I saw him at the Palla-
    dium. And we all screamed because he was so fab.
    He has eyes like great blue pools . . . and long, gor-
    geous hair that shone in the lights. And he wore a suit
    with tight trousers and a polo-necked sweater.... And
    he sang this song about a girl he had lost. And it was
    called . . . 'Fading Love'. (*The other two give great
    romantic sighs.*)

> THE GIRLS *exit down the street. As they sigh, the gang's
> heads appear above the wall, all with horrified expressions
> on their faces and holding their noses as though they had
> just smelt a bad smell.*

ALL: Poo! (*They climb on to the wall.*)
CARROTS: Girls is horrid.
SPARKS: Have you ever thought what it must be like
    to be a girl?
NYLON: Crumbs, Sparks, please!
PUFF: Cor, Sparks, shurrup – it's too awful on top of
    breakfast.
SPARKS: No, but serious – have you? Drooling on like
    that about boys. (*He jumps down from the wall, takes up*

a mock-girl's stance and then imitates mockingly.) OOO
and he was fabulous . . . You should have seen his
eyes! Like mucky pools! And his hair . . . OOO . . .
fab! Like tangled fuse wire! And he sang the most fab
song called (*he jumps down and grabs* WRIGGLES *as
though making love*) 'My Love for You is Like Mouldy
Custard'.

They are all giggling.

WRIGGLES: Hey but, Sparks, she didn't say that. She
said . . .

PUFF: Gag him, Sparks!

They jump down and gather round WRIGGLES.

NYLON: Poor Wriggles. You just don't understand.

PUFF: But you will one day. When you is old as us and
know about girls, you'll understand.

CARROTS: Take a tip from me, Wriggles. Have nothing
to do with them. I don't. Leave them strictly alone.

WRIGGLES: But I like girls.

ALL: What!

JOHNNY *and* SPARKS *grab* WRIGGLES *by the elbows
and stand him on the dustbin.*

JOHNNY (*scandalized*): But Wriggles, you can't. I mean,
well, I mean. You just *can't*!

WRIGGLES: Oh! Why?

SPARKS: It's not allowed. It's high treason.

WRIGGLES: Oh? What's that?

SPARKS: Well – you know – like, it's against the gang.

JOHNNY: Yes. It's against us.

PUFF: Anyway, Wriggles, you ain't old enough to like
girls.

NYLON: No. You ain't old enough.

WRIGGLES: How old do you have to be then?

CARROTS: Honest, Wriggles! You're *never* old enough
    − leave them strictly alone.

PUFF: Look, Carrots, shut up. What do you know
    about it? After all, you're only a girl.

JOHNNY (*being fatherly and adult*): You see, Wriggles,
    it's like this . . . Girls are not like boys. Well . . . you
    know . . . Girls is girls and boys is boys.

WRIGGLES: I know, Johnny. That's why I like girls.

JOHNNY: But, Wriggles, you can't. Well, look. You
    see . . . Oh, crumbs! Hasn't your Dad told you any-
    thing yet?

WRIGGLES: Anything about what?

JOHNNY: About girls.

WRIGGLES: Dunno . . . Nothing what I can remember.

SPARKS: Well, has he talked to you about . . . well about
    the birds and the bees?

WRIGGLES: No, don't think so. (*Pause.*) Oh yes he did!

ALL (*very eager and crowding round*): Did he? What did
    he say?

WRIGGLES: He said that if I didn't keep away from that
    bloody bee it would sting me.

    They are all exasperated. JOHNNY, SPARKS *and*
    WRIGGLES *go to the wall by the lamp-post.* WRIGGLES
    begins to climb it.

NYLON: It's no use. He's too young.

PUFF: But he likes girls. That's bad for him.

NYLON: Yeah. But he'll grow out of it. I liked girls once.

CARROTS: If he's not careful he'll turn out to be a
    regular Casanova. Like that Bouncer Barton. Don't
    like him. Thinks he's the tops.

PUFF: Yeah. I reckon someone ought to poke his nose.
    Big bully, he is.

JOHNNY: Away you go then, Puff. You're just the man.

PUFF: Not just now thanks. I'm a bit busy.

WRIGGLES (*from half-way up the lamp-post*): It's all right,
Puff. You needn't worry about being busy.

PUFF: Why not?

WRIGGLES: Cos he's here. He's coming up the street.

ALL: WHAT!

JOHNNY: Come on!

They disappear over the wall again leaving WRIGGLES
clinging to the lamp-post.

WRIGGLES: Hey! Wait on. (*He tries to get down and
cannot.*) Oh! Help! (*Not able to get down, he decides to
climb farther up and at last hangs from the ladder-bar.*)

Enter BOUNCER, BIFF *and* SMIG. *They are brash, and
behave like what they know themselves to be: the local
toughs.*

BOUNCER: Hello! Hello! Hello! What's this then?
Britain's champion lamp-post climber! Look at that,
boys. Wriggles the monkey, straight out of the zoo.

*They all giggle maliciously, and gather under the lamp-
post.* BOUNCER *catches hold of* WRIGGLES's *voluminous
shorts.*

BOUNCER: What's this then, Wriggles, my lamb? Dad's
drain-pipes? (*He pulls.*) Ooopsee! Well now, look at
that. His pants are coming down.

WRIGGLES: Gerroff! Give me my pants back!

BOUNCER: Stop squawking, monkey.

JOHNNY's *head appears above the wall.*

JOHNNY: Lay off him. (*He jumps on to the wall. The
others appear and look over at* BOUNCER.)

BOUNCER: Well, well, if it isn't mighty mouse himself.

SMIG: I think the mouse said something, Bouncer.

BIFF: Yea. Did you hear him squeak?

BOUNCER: We was just having a friendly chat with your monkey – er, I mean your pal – here, Salter, my lad.

JOHNNY (*he jumps down in front of* BOUNCER): Lay off him!

BIFF: He did squeak, you know, Bouncer. I heard him distinctly that time.

WRIGGLES: Get me down, Johnny. I'm stuck!

BOUNCER: Oh! Poor monkey. He's stuck, boys. Give the ape a hand. Do what he says. Get him down.

    BIFF *and* SMIGG *lift* WRIGGLES *down, making it very unpleasant for him.* JOHNNY's *gang shout their protests at the manhandling. Finally* BOUNCER *grabs* WRIGGLES *and throws him into* JOHNNY's *arms.*

BOUNCER: There's your pet, Salter. You ought to look after him better.

BIFF: Yeah. There's a law against monkeys running wild.

SMIG: Yeah, poor thing. You ought to be reported to the R.S.P.C.A. for cruelty to tame monkeys.

JOHNNY (*advancing in a rage*): Look, Barton, if you want a poke in the eye, you just go on like that.

BOUNCER: Oh, ho! Fighting talk. You wouldn't be thinking of having your mates empty some dustbins all over me would you? Like last week? Cos if you were I might just have to bounce you, Salter, my lad.

JOHNNY: You can have a fair fight any time you want, Barton, if that's what's bothering you.

BOUNCER: Well now, that might be just up my street, now you come to mention it.

SPARKS (*jumping down between them*): No, Johnny! Don't be daft!

BOUNCER (*grabbing* SPARKS *and pulling him close*): Come

now, Sparkler, old chap, surely you aren't scared? I mean, I could understand it if it was you that had to fight. But not when it's your big, brave bossman.

SPARKS (*pushing away from* BOUNCER's *hold*): Belt up, Barton. Johnny could beat you any day. If the fight was fair. Only that's something you can't do – fight fair.

BOUNCER: Do you hear that, Smig? Do you hear him, Biff? The little man says I don't fight fair.

BIFF *and* SMIG *close in.*

SMIG: I hear him, Bouncer.

BIFF: I think you ought to teach them a lesson, Bouncer.

BOUNCER: Now you might have a point there, Biff. (*To* JOHNNY.) Take your shirt off, Salter. (BOUNCER *and gang take up their position by the wall and lamp-post.* JOHNNY *takes off his shirt and sits on the dustbin.* WRIGGLES *takes the shirt and uses it as a towel, fanning* JOHNNY *vigorously with it.* SPARKS *and* CARROTS *act as seconds, loudly giving* JOHNNY *technical advice.* PUFF *and* NYLON *sit up on the wall.* PUFF *acts as time-keeper – he's the only one with a watch;* NYLON *produces a dustbin lid from behind the wall, which he uses as a gong.*)

NYLON: Seconds out. (*He bangs the lid.*) Round One!

Everyone retreats to the edges, shouting advice. JOHNNY *takes up a very exaggerated boxer's stance;* BOUNCER *walks round patronizingly, slowly rubbing a clenched fist in the palm of his other hand. After circling each other* JOHNNY *is knocked down. He recovers, dives at* BOUNCER *whom he clumps hard in the chest.* BOUNCER *falls into the arms of* BIFF *and* SMIG. JOHNNY's *gang cheer madly.*

NYLON (*banging the lid triumphantly, bellows*): End of Round One.

At once SPARKS *and* CARROTS *rush in, seat* JOHNNY *on the dustbin and prepare him for the next round, just as they have seen seconds do on TV.* WRIGGLES *fans with the towel even more vigorously.* BOUNCER *holds serious conversation with his henchmen. He is obviously laying a plan.*

NYLON: Seconds out! (*He bangs the lid.*) Round Two.

JOHNNY'S *seconds rush out of the 'ring'.* JOHNNY *bounds up, and makes for* BOUNCER, *standing with his back to* JOHNNY.

BIFF (*as* JOHNNY *closes in*): NOW!

BOUNCER *side-steps.* BIFF *and* SMIG *grab* JOHNNY *and push him backwards.* BOUNCER *sticks out a foot and trips* JOHNNY *as he recoils from* BIFF *and* SMIG. JOHNNY *falls and* BOUNCER *dives on to him. They struggle.* JOHNNY'S *gang shout in protest and attack* BIFF *and* SMIG. NYLON *remains watching from the wall. Even* WRIGGLES *helps by repeatedly kicking the backside of* SMIG *who is engaged with* CARROTS *and* PUFF. SPARKS *and* BIFF *carry on war together.*

Enter the POLICEMAN.

POLICEMAN: All right . . . all right . . . come on . . . cut it out. What's going on then?

The fight hurriedly breaks up. They all assume exaggerated friendliness, as though nothing had happened, except WRIGGLES *who storms up to the* POLICEMAN.

WRIGGLES: He fouled Johnny and Johnny would have won. You ought to arrest him.

JOHNNY: Shut up, Wriggles! (*To the* POLICEMAN.) It's all right, honest.

POLICEMAN: What's all right? What were you fighting over, eh?

WRIGGLES: It was . . .

JOHNNY: Shut up, Wriggles! (WRIGGLES *stamps his foot and gives up huffily.*) Nothing really. It was just . . . Well, just a friendly contest, like.

POLICEMAN: A friendly contest, eh? Then you've a funny idea of friendliness. (*He goes to* BARTON.) What have you to say to that, young Barton?

> BOUNCER *eyes the* POLICEMAN *arrogantly.*

BOUNCER: It was like he says. A friendly fight.

POLICEMAN (*growing annoyed*): Now look here, you bonny lot. If you want to batter the living daylights out of each other, do it in your own back gardens, not out here in the street, do you hear?

BIFF (*archly*): Our house hasn't got a back garden, Constable!

POLICEMAN (*going up to* BIFF): Any more of your lip, lad, and you'll feel the weight of my hand.

BIFF: Don't you threaten me – I'll get a policeman. (*He goes to* BOUNCER.) The man's getting hard, Bouncer!

BOUNCER: Oh, shut up and let's go. (*To* JOHNNY.) I'll get you later, Salter.

JOHNNY: Any time, Barton.

> *Exit* BOUNCER.

> SMIG *saunters up to the* POLICEMAN *cheekily.*

BIFF: So long, Constable.

> *Exit* BIFF *singing:*

> Whip away the blue-tailed fly!
> Oh! Jimmy crack horn and I don't care! . . .
> Jimmy crack horn and I don't care. . . .

As his voice goes off down the street JOHNNY'S *gang all turn on* SMIG, *who grows more and more uncomfortable* *until at last he edges away and finally rushes off **down the** street.*

Exit SMIG.

The gang settle into groups. The POLICEMAN *joins* JOHNNY *who is sitting on a wall, downcast.*

POLICEMAN: Now look, young Salter, take my tip and keep away from that Barton gang. They're up to no good, and they'll only get you into trouble.

SPARKS: It wasn't Johnny's fault. He couldn't help it, honest, Constable.

JOHNNY: Shut up, Sparks, will you?

WRIGGLES: Yeah, and Johnny would have won, wouldn't he, Puff?

PUFF: Yeah, wouldn't he, Nylon?

NYLON: Yeah, wouldn't you, Johnny?

JOHNNY (*exasperated*): Shut up, will you!

POLICEMAN: Look, lad. I wasn't born yesterday. And I've seen you and Barton having flare-ups before around here, and I suppose sometimes you've got to have it out fair and square. But Barton never plays fair, so look out.

SPARKS: That's what I said, isn't it, chaps? (*They all agree.*)

POLICEMAN: So keep away, boy Be sensible.

JOHNNY: It's O.K. Honest. It's not that I don't believe you or anything. But sometimes you've got to fight back, haven't you? Even when you know the other chap won't be fair. You can't just run away every time, can you? If you did, you wouldn't be able to look people in the face. You would be just a coward. Anyway, he's *always* picking on Wriggles, and Wriggles is too small to look after himself. Somebody has to help him. You can't just stand there and watch them muck him about.

POLICEMAN: But can't you see? He only does it to get you annoyed. He just wants to make you lose your temper, because he knows he'll get the better of you then and the laugh will be on you.

JOHNNY: I didn't lose my temper today.

SPARKS: No, and he didn't fight fair today.

JOHNNY: Look, lay off will you! Anybody would think I'd done a major crime, the way you lot are going on.

POLICEMAN: All right, son. We're only trying to help. But take care, that's all. Bouncer Barton isn't worth the bother. Don't say I haven't warned you. (*Exit* POLICEMAN.)

The others, aware of JOHNNY's *mood, leave him and lounge in a group away from him. They are very deflated. Then* WRIGGLES *takes a train-spotter's book from his pocket, very deliberately hides it behind his back, and crosses to* JOHNNY. *He climbs on to the wall and sits beside* JOHNNY. *He looks at him closely.* JOHNNY *remains still, staring at the ground.*

WRIGGLES (*quietly*): You wasn't half good, Johnny. (*Pause.*) You would have beat him easy, Johnny. I know you could.

JOHNNY (*flatly*): Thanks, Wriggles.

WRIGGLES (*very seriously*): Johnny. . . ?

JOHNNY: Yeah?

WRIGGLES: You know my new train-spotting book?

JOHNNY: Yeah?

WRIGGLES (*producing the book from behind his back*): This one, my Dad bought me yesterday?

JOHNNY: Yeah?

WRIGGLES: Well, Johnny . . . would you like it?

JOHNNY (*starting up*): Your new train book?

WRIGGLES: Yes. Not just for a lend, Johnny . . . for keeps. I could easy get another one, and I thought how you might like a new one, cos you haven't bought one for ages and well . . . (*gently.*) I want you to have it, Johnny.

JOHNNY (*brightly*): Crumbs, Wriggles, that's smart of you. But, well . . . I'm past train-spotting now, and you'll use it more than me. But it's great of you to offer it me, Wriggles. Thanks. I say, I'll tell you what. I'll take you down to Joe's Place and buy you a double ice sundae. How's that?

WRIGGLES: A double . . . Crikey, Johnny. A double iced sundae! . . .

JOHNNY: Say, you lot, come on. I'm going to buy Wriggles an ice-cream at Joe's. You coming?
   They perk up.

PUFF: Yeah. I am anyhow. I'm hungry after that exercise. Fighting is hard work. Seems as if I never had any breakfast at all.

SPARKS: Honest, Puff, you're just a guts.

PUFF: Well, as my Dad says: you've got to keep life and limb together.

NYLON: Your Dad ain't seen his limbs for years: his stomach's too big to see over.

PUFF: Ha, Ha! Better than being starvation on stilts like you.

SPARKS: Tell you what. Race you to Joe's. (*He gets on his bicycle.*)

JOHNNY: You're on!

WRIGGLES: What about me?

JOHNNY: Come on, Wriggles, up you get. (WRIGGLES
climbs on to JOHNNY's *back.*)

SPARKS: Now then – last one to Joe's is a cissy. Ready . . .
steady . . . go. (*They race off.* PUFF *trips and sprawls.*
NYLON *falls over* PUFF *and bounds up.*)

NYLON: Oh, look . . . mind my shirt. My Mother'll kill
me. (*Exit* NYLON.)

PUFF (*staggering to his feet*). Hey, you chaps, wait for me.
(*Exit* PUFF.)

CURTAIN

SCENE TWO

JOE'S PLACE, *later the same morning. A counter with high
stools, mugs, drinks. Two tables with stools, one down
right, the other down left.*

SALLY GRIMSHAW *sits on a stool at the counter, talking to*
JOE, *who is cleaning the tables and tidying up.*

JOE: Are you sure you want the job?

SALLY: Yes, Mr Hobson.

JOE: Call me Joe. Everybody does.

SALLY: Yes, Mr Hobson.

JOE: But I can't think why a girl like you wants a job
in a place like this, washing up and waiting and such.
Not with a Dad like yours. You know?

SALLY: My parents think it's a good idea for me to earn
some of my own pocket-money. And there's no other
jobs going that I want.

JOE: Aye, well, so long as your parents don't mind, I don't suppose I should.

SALLY: No, Mr Hobson.

JOE: Joe!

SALLY: . . . Joe.

JOE: Well now, as I say. You'll wash up, and wait on a bit when we're busy and maybe, when you've got the hang of the place, you can take care of it when I'm out for lunch and such.

SALLY: Yes, Mr . . . Joe.

JOE: We're not so busy on a Saturday morning, because everybody goes into town, like. But in the evenings when you come in after school there'll be plenty to do.

SALLY: Yes, Joe.

Enter MOGGS *from the street.*

MOGGS: Morning, Joe.

JOE: Morning, Harry. Want your bait?

MOGGS: Aye, if it's ready.

JOE: Sally, go and get Mr Moggs's bait out of the back.

SALLY: Mr Moggs's bait, Joe?

JOE: Aye, his food for work.

SALLY: Oh! I thought you meant food for fishing with!

JOE: He gets it every day, don't you, Harry?

MOGGS: That's right, Joe. Have done for years. It's out the back on the table.

Exit SALLY *to the kitchen.*

MOGGS: New girl then, Joe?

JOE: Aye. Started this morning. You'll have to mind your P's and Q's when you come in here now, lad.

MOGGS: Mind me P's and Q's? What for?

JOE: Well, don't you recognize who she is?

MOGGS: The girl? No. Who?

JOE: Sally Grimshaw. The Grimshaws' daughter. Your boss.

MOGGS: What? You mean Grimshaw of the mill? That one?

JOE: Aye. Your boss.

MOGGS: Well, I never! The old slave-driver. Sending his *daughter* out to work now.

JOE: Just what I thought. But no. She says she wants to. Wants to earn some of her own pocket-money.

MOGGS: If her Dad's as mean with her as he is with the men, she'll *need* to earn some of her own pocket-money, if you ask me. Funny folk, the Grimshaws.

JOE: You can say that again.

MOGGS: Funny folk the Grimshaws. Will she cope, do you think?

JOE: Dunno, Harry. Wait and see. Can't get labour these days. Not in a place like this. Want all the glamour of them caffs in town, with their musical boxes and express coffee machines. But here! (*Pause.*) I heard there's some trouble at the mill.

MOGGS: Aye. Pinching stuff out of the warehouse. I can't trace it. Old Grimshaw's going mad.

JOE: Well I never.

MOGGS: Well, yer see there's no clue as to how they get the stuff out. Not a trace. They've watched the day men till they're sick. So Grimshaw says it *must* be me. Can't convince him otherwise neither.

JOE: There's nought so queer as folk, Harry.

MOGGS: It's not folk, Joe, just Grimshaw, as worries me.

Enter SALLY. *She has put an overall on.*

SALLY: I can't find it, Joe. It's not on the table.

JOE: Never mind, lass. Haven't got the hang of the place yet I don't expect. I'll come and show yer.

MOGGS: Look, Joe. I'm just popping down the town. I'll call in on the way back and have me dinner and take me bait.

JOE: All right, Harry. See you.

Exit JOE *and* SALLY *to the kitchen. Exit* MOGGS *to the street. A pause. Enter* JOHNNY, *running, with* WRIGGLES *on his back.* JOHNNY *flops on to a high stool, after sitting* WRIGGLES *on the counter. Enter* SPARKS, *puffing.*

JOHNNY: Beat you!

SPARKS: Wouldn't have done, if that woman hadn't had that pram all over the pavement.

Enter NYLON, *who flops down at a table.*

NYLON: Puff's a bit behind. He tripped. Come to think of it, Puff's all behind!

Enter CARROTS *who wanders round, looking for* JOE.

CARROTS: Joe's not here.

Enter PUFF *who flops down beside* NYLON. *He is exhausted.*

PUFF: You tripped me! It isn't fair!

NYLON: Go on, tank. You tripped yourself.

CARROTS: Joe's not here!

JOHNNY: Course he is. Must be.

WRIGGLES: Must be. Cos the shop's open. (*He shouts.*) Joe!

SPARKS: Bet he's out the back.

WRIGGLES (*shouts*): Joe!

PUFF: Here, let's hide and ambush him.

NYLON: Kids' stuff!

SPARKS: Yeah. Come on. Behind the counter, Carrots Go on.

CARROTS *hides behind the counter.* WRIGGLES, JOHNNY *and* SPARKS *hide at the opposite end of the counter from the kitchen entrance.* PUFF *and* NYLON *hide behind the stools at the table nearest the kitchen entrance.*

A pause. Then WRIGGLES *giggles, jumps up and yells.*

WRIGGLES: Joe!

NYLON: Shurrup, Wriggles!

JOHNNY *pulls* WRIGGLES *down again. Pause. Enter* SALLY *with a tray of mugs, followed by* JOE.

SPARKS *(jumping up)*: Stigem up!

They all come out with great noise. SALLY *screams and drops the tray. The gang stand aghast.*

JOE: Good heavens, boys! What you doing?

WRIGGLES: OO! Crikey!

NYLON: Sorry, Joe.

PUFF: We was just ambushing you.

SPARKS: Thought you was alone.

JOE: Ah, well. Nought broken. Clear up the mess.

JOHNNY *gets down and helps* SALLY *pick up the dropped things. He is obviously fascinated by* SALLY *and looks at her all the time. The others gather round the counter with* JOE, *casting curious glances at* SALLY.

SPARKS *(confidentially)*: Who's that then, Joe?

JOE: New girl. Started today, helping out.

SPARKS: Don't like girls. What you want to have a girl for? Could have had a boy.

JOE: None for the job.

SPARKS: If you'd have asked me I'd have done it. Specially if I'd known it was a girl what was going to have it.

WRIGGLES *(to* SALLY*)*: Here, I haven't seen you before.

SALLY: No. I'm new. I help Mr Hobson.

PUFF: Mr Hobson! (*They all roar with laughter.*)

NYLON: Here, Joe. She called you Mr Hobson.

JOE: That's me.

ALL *(except JOHNNY)*: Mr Hobson! (*Laughter again.*)

WRIGGLES: What's your name then?

SALLY: Sally.

CARROTS. (*winking at SPARKS*): Sally? (*She sings, mockingly.*) Sally . . . Sally . . . Right down our alley.

SPARKS, PUFF, NYLON and WRIGGLES (*join in to make a raucous chorus*): You are the one for me. (*Much laughter.*)

NYLON: You helping, do you say?

SALLY: Yes.

NYLON: Helping break stuff eh? (*Laughter.*)

PUFF: Having a smashing time, she is. (*Laughter.*)

SPARKS: If he'd have asked me, I'd have done the job.

NYLON: Go on, Sparks, you couldn't boil a kettle.

CARROTS: What you want to work here for?

SALLY: To earn some pocket-money.

JOHNNY: Doesn't your Dad give you any then?

SALLY: Only a little.

WRIGGLES: Must be mingey, your Dad.

PUFF: All dads is mingey!

SALLY: No. Really. I *want* to have a job. It's more fun than just staying at home.

NYLON: Don't she talk posh!

WRIGGLES: Yeah. Posh! You don't come from round here, do you?

SPARKS: Honest, Wriggles, you aren't half thick. Couldn't you see straight away she doesn't? We'd have seen her before if she did. I'd have *certainly* done the job for you, Joe, if I'd have known you was *that* short.

SALLY: I think you're very rude.

SPARKS (*aghast*): Did you hear that!?

JOE: Now then, boys. Sally's got work to do. Leave her
alone.

The gang gather round JOE, *who begins pouring out
drinks.*

ALL: But, Joe. Honest. You can't take her on. Let us do
it, Joe. She's a *girl*. She's a girl from the other side of
town. I'll do the job for you. *etc.* . . .

The light and sound fades until JOHNNY *and* SALLY *are
left sitting at a table, pooled in warm light. They are a little
shy of each other, but gain confidence as they talk together.*

JOHNNY: Don't mind them.

SALLY: I don't. But they *are* rude.

JOHNNY: They don't mean it. Not really.

SALLY: Then they shouldn't say those things.

JOHNNY: It's just that . . . well . . . we always come here.
It's sort of a meeting place for us. And we think of it
as ours. And then to find you here suddenly . . . well
. . . they don't like it. Haven't got used to it yet. They'll
be all right when they get used to you.

SALLY: Are you a sort of gang?

JOHNNY: Yeah. We're always together. We do everything together.

SALLY: That must be fun. I've never been in a gang.

JOHNNY: Haven't you? I thought everybody was in a
gang. There's lots round here.

SALLY: My parents don't like gangs.

JOHNNY: Oh! I know how it is. Parents are difficult
sometimes.

*They are silent for a moment. There is a roar of laughter
from the gang.*

SALLY: Do you ever get tired of them?

JOHNNY: Sometimes. You know? I've got fed up of train spotting and playing kids' games. But somehow, you can't just leave them. They wouldn't understand. At least not Wriggles and Puff. Sparks is all right. He's the one who frightened you.

SALLY: I don't think I'd like him.

JOHNNY: He's all right, honest. Only he doesn't like girls.

SALLY: Do you?

JOHNNY (*looks uncomfortable*): Dunno. I haven't really tried them yet.

SALLY: Oh.

JOHNNY: Do you like boys?

SALLY: Dunno. Haven't really tried them yet.

They laugh gently together. Pause.

JOHNNY (*suddenly having a bright thought*): Look – I've got a smashing idea. Why don't you come with me to the club tonight? You could meet the gang and maybe get to know them and then they wouldn't be so rude to you about working here. How about it?

SALLY: I'd love to, really I would. But . . .

JOHNNY: Well?

SALLY: My Father always makes me bring friends home first before he'll let me go out with them.

JOHNNY: That's O.K. I don't mind meeting your Dad. I could come this afternoon, and then you could come to the club tonight.

SALLY: What sort of club is it?

JOHNNY: It's the youth club we go to. We're doing a pantomime for Christmas and our leader's looking for a principal girl. Here. Maybe you'd do. Have you ever acted before?

SALLY: I don't think I could do that. I've only acted at school in form plays and things.

JOHNNY: That's all right. It's easy. Anyway you could come and see, couldn't you? . . . Go on.

SALLY: All right. But you'll have to see Daddy first. At tea, this afternoon. About 4.30, O.K.?

JOHNNY: O.K. Here! But I dunno your name, or where you live.

SALLY: My name's Sally Grimshaw, and I live at High-fields on the Moorlands Road.

JOHNNY (*shattered*): You don't mean your Dad is old Grimshaw that owns . . .

SALLY: Yes, didn't you know?

JOHNNY: O, Lor!

SALLY: What's the matter?

JOHNNY: I . . . yer . . . the . . . Oh crumbs!

SALLY: It's all right. Daddy's all right, really. Don't forget. 4.30. He can't bear people who are late.

The lights return suddenly to normal. BOUNCER, BIFF *and* SMIG *are standing by* JOHNNY'S *table, grinning widely.*

BOUNCER: Watcher, mates! It's your old friend, Bouncer.

The gang moan painfully.

WRIGGLES: O, crikey! It's He-man again. He's a bit thick, he is, Joe.

SMIG: The little man's talking again, Bouncer.

BOUNCER: That's O.K., Smig. Live and let live, yer know. Hello, Joe.

JOE: Now, Barton, boy. Up to mischief again?

BOUNCER: Aw, now, Joe. Them's not nice things to say.

JOE: My recollection of you, young Barton, is that you're not nice to know.

BIFF: Welcoming, ain't they, Bouncer?

BOUNCER: It's a hard world, Biff. Would you have any objection to serving us, Joe?

JOE: Not so long as you behave yourselves, that's all.

SMIG: But we always behave ourselves, Joe!

PUFF (*mocking*): Ha! Ha!

    SMIG *is about to make a move at* PUFF *but* BOUNCER *prevents him.*

BOUNCER: We'll have a coke each, *please*, Joe.

    JOE *prepares a tray with three drinks on it.* BOUNCER *returns to* JOHNNY.

BOUNCER: Well, well. Having a nice cosy chat, aren't we! Shall we join them, Smig?

SMIG: Yeah, let's.

JOHNNY: Hop it, Barton!

BOUNCER: There's politeness for you, Biff.

BIFF: Yeah, right in front of his girl friend here.

JOHNNY (*roused, makes for* BOUNCER): Look you . . .

    JOE *walks between them, tray in hand.*

JOE: Just as I thought. Trouble the minute you come into the place, Barton.

BOUNCER: Come off it, Joe. It was him that made the move.

JOE: Never mind about that, lad. One more wrong word out of you and out you go. Now mind. Go and sit yourselves over there.

    BOUNCER *glares arrogantly at* JOE *who glares back.*

Then BOUNCER *throws some coins contemptuously on to the tray and snatches his drink.* BIFF *and* SMIG *copy his example and follow* BOUNCER *to the other table.*

JOE: Sally, go out back and finish the dishes.

Exit SALLY. JOE *returns to the counter.* JOHNNY *slumps despondently into his seat at the table. The light and sound fades again, leaving* BOUNCER *and gang pooled in a cold, hard light at their table.*

BOUNCER (*grinning*): That got him!

BIFF: Right rattled he was.

SMIG: Pity that Joe bust in. Might have scrambled Salter that time.

BOUNCER: Aye. But I haven't finished with him yet, not after this morning I haven't.

SMIG: What you going to do, Bouncer?

BOUNCER (*very secretive*): What am I going to do? Now listen. Remember I told you we had to lay off pinching stuff out of Grimshaw's warehouse cos the police was getting wise, and things was too hot?

BIFF and SMIG: Yeah.

SMIG: Getting too hot, you said. We'd be caught if we did much more.

BOUNCER: Right, Smig. Well we're going to do one more little job there.

SMIG: What for, Bouncer, if we might get nabbed?

BOUNCER: Not *might*, Smig. *Will*.

BIFF: But what do you *want* to get caught for, Bouncer?

BOUNCER: Cos it won't be *us* what gets caught, Biff.

BIFF: Then who, Bouncer?

BOUNCER: Salter. Johnny Salter.

BIFF and SMIG (*loudly*): Johnny Salter! But . . .

BOUNCER (*silencing them hurriedly*): Shurrup, you clots!

(*He looks about.*) Honest, sometimes I wonder why I lumber myself with you two. It's like this. He'll be at the club tonight, won't he?

BIFF: Yeah.

BOUNCER: And so will we.

SMIG: Will we?

BOUNCER: We will! And, quite accidently, you understand, we'll get Salter annoyed. But he won't fight there. Not in the club. So we'll dare him to do something else instead.

BIFF: Crikey, Bouncer. What'll we dare him?

BOUNCER: You know, Biff, you must have a brain the size of a pea. And a split pea at that. Can't you see? We'll dare him to go into Grimshaw's and flog something that'll prove he's been there. Something small, yer see, that won't bother his honest little conscience.

SMIG: But what if he won't?

BOUNCER: He will, you'll see.

BIFF: Maybe. But that doesn't mean he'll get caught. Not for certain.

BOUNCER: It does, if we phone the police when he's in there, and tell them we seen someone going in.

SMIG: Cor, Bouncer. That's pretty good.

BOUNCER: Of course, Smig. No flies on me, yer know.

BIFF: Here, but, Bouncer. What if Salter gets out before the police get there?

BOUNCER: Simple, Biff, my boy. Remember Moggs, that nightwatchman, is in there an' all.

BIFF: Yeah.

BOUNCER: Well, if he catches Salter at it, he'll hang on to him till the police gets there.

BIFF: That's all right. But how do we know he *will* catch Salter?

BOUNCER: Cos I'll be there to see he does.

SMIG: You will?

BOUNCER: Yes. Why not? I know every inch of that place. Ought to, the jobs we done there. I'll see that Salter gets to the right place, then see the lights are switched on just at the right time, and scarper.

BIFF: But what if Salter says you was with him?

BOUNCER: Don't talk daft. D'you think anybody would believe him? After the bust-ups we've had? They'd think he was just saying it out of spite.

SMIG: Yeah, they would. That's flipping marvellous, Bouncer. You aren't half a one! Wish I could think up summat like that.

BOUNCER: You will, Smig. One day, you will.

The light returns to normal suddenly. The gang are jeering at PUFF, *who advances centre with a mug.*

PUFF: I bet I *can* balance one of them mugs on my forehead.

NYLON: Nonsense!

JOE: Don't you go breaking them mugs all over my place.

PUFF: It's all right, Joe. You'll see. Look. (*He does it, but* NYLON *comes up behind and jabs him in the ribs.* PUFF *has a retaliatory skirmish.*)

NYLON: Mind my pullover!

SPARKS: That's nothing. Come here, Wriggles.

WRIGGLES: What, Sparks?

SPARKS: Get up on my shoulders.

WRIGGLES: What for?

SPARKS: Just get up, that's all.

WRIGGLES climbs on to SPARKS's *shoulders.*

JOE: Careful, lad. Don't drop him.

SPARKS: It's O.K., Joe. We've done this often. Now, Wriggles, do the famous balancing act. (*He hands* WRIGGLES *a mug.*)

WRIGGLES: Oo, yes. I like that. (WRIGGLES *balances the mug on his head. The gang cheer. Enter* MOGGS.)

MOGGS: Hello, Joe. Hello, boys.

WRIGGLES: Moggs! (*The mug flies off his head in his excitement and lands in* MOGGS's *hands, followed by* WRIGGLES.)

BOUNCER: Come on, men. This place is like a nursery. *They get up and walk over to* JOHNNY.

BOUNCER: See you at the club tonight, Salter.

JOHNNY: Worse luck!

BIFF: Charming!

SMIG: Friendly!

BOUNCER: Come on. (*Exit* BOUNCER *and* GANG *to street.*)

Enter SALLY *from kitchen.*

SALLY: I've finished in here, Joe.

JOE: All right, dear. Go home for your dinner.

SALLY: Thanks, Joe. I'll be back at one.

JOE: All right, Sally.

Exit SALLY *to street.*

THE GANG (*mocking*): Bye, bye, Sally, etc. . . .

Exit JOE *to kitchen.*

MOGGS: What's up with Johnny then? You sulking, son? *They gather round him.*

WRIGGLES: Yeah. What's the matter, Johnny?

SPARKS: Is it that Barton lot?

JOHNNY: Nothing. No, not really.

NYLON: What you sitting there all by yourself for then?

JOHNNY: Nothing, honest, Nylon.

MOGGS: Come on, lad, spill the beans.

JOHNNY: Do you know old Grimshaw, Moggs?

MOGGS: Grimshaw? Course. I work for him.

JOHNNY: What's *he* like?

MOGGS: What you asking for, lad?

WRIGGLES: Yeah. What you want to know for, Johnny?

JOHNNY (*looking sick*): I've got to have tea with him today.

   The GANG *are astounded.*

MOGGS: Tea. With Grimshaw. What for?

JOHNNY: Cos I want to take Sally to the club tonight.

   MOGGS *roars with laughter. The* GANG *are puzzled.*

SPARKS: What do you mean, Johnny?

JOHNNY: I thought she might get to know you there.

SPARKS: Who?

JOHNNY: The girl. Sally. The new girl here.

SPARKS: You don't mean you're taking that new girl to the club!

JOHNNY: Yeah. Why not?

   Pause. The GANG *are aghast.*

SPARKS: He's off his head.

NYLON: Gone mad he has.

CARROTS: You feeling well, Johnny?

JOHNNY: Look. What's so odd about taking a girl to the club? It's happened before.

PUFF: Maybe. But not to you it hasn't.

SPARKS (*with growing anger*): No. Betraying the gang, that's what it is.

JOHNNY (*provoked to anger too*): I'm not betraying anybody. I just thought it would be good if she came to the club and got to know us. She has to work here. She might as well get to like us.

SPARKS: Like US! Come off it. *We* don't like GIRLS.

JOHNNY: Crikey, Sparks! GROW UP!

    Tense silence.

MOGGS: Now then, now then. Damage is done now, isn't it? Sit down, lad. (*They sit.*) But why do you have to have tea with Grimshaw?

JOHNNY: Cos Grimshaw is her Father and doesn't let her go out without he's seen her friends first.

SPARKS: Grimshaw. *HER* Father! (*He bursts into laughter. The GANG join him.*)

MOGGS: Didn't Joe tell you?

JOHNNY (*crestfallen*): No. I didn't know till she told me. And I'd fixed it by then. Look, Moggs. You got to help. I've never been and had tea with anybody like Grimshaw before.

WRIGGLES: I bet it won't half be awful, Johnny.

JOHNNY: Thanks for the comfort, Wriggles!

CARROTS: Look, Johnny, don't go.

JOHNNY: I've got to. I said I would, so I've got to.

PUFF: What for? You could say you was ill or something.

JOHNNY: You can't just do things like that, Puff. I got to go, and that's it. What do I do, Moggs?

MOGGS: Invited for tea, are you? About 4.30?

JOHNNY: Yes.

MOGGS: Get there on the dot. Grimshaw can't stand folk who are late.

JOHNNY: That's what Sally said.

MOGGS: Be nice as pie. Very polite. Call him Sir. Drink your tea, eat a bit of cake. Say thank you for the invitation, and shoot off home.

JOHNNY: Is that all?

MOGGS: You'll find that's quite enough for one day.

JOHNNY: What if he asks all sorts of awkward questions?

MOGGS: Knowing Grimshaw, he will. But don't worry. He won't eat you – well, not all. Just use your loaf, give him a straight honest answer, and hope. If the lassie wants to come with you enough, she'll see things turn out all right.

WRIGGLES: Rather you than me, Johnny.

JOHNNY: Thanks, Wriggles.

CARROTS: I went to tea with my Headmistress once. It was awful!

PUFF: I'll bet!

NYLON: Awful!

SPARKS: Look, Johnny. You can't go. Honest.

JOHNNY: Hard luck, Sparks! I'm going.

Enter JOE, *carrying a huge ice-cream sundae.*

JOE: Here you are. Here's the double iced sundae you asked for.

JOHNNY: There you are, Wriggles. It's on me.

WRIGGLES (*rushing delightedly to Joe*): Thanks, Johnny. I've always wanted one of these. (*He takes it to* JOHNNY.) Look, Johnny! (*In his enthusiasm,* WRIGGLES *trips, falls and puts his face into the sundae. He stands up, his face covered in ice-cream. The others roar with glee.*)

NYLON: Did you say it was on you, Johnny? Cos it's on Wriggles now!

Gales of laughter.

CURTAIN

ACT TWO

The garden of the GRIMSHAWS', *local factory owners. A warm sunny afternoon the same Saturday. A wall; suggestion of trees, flowers and grass. A garden table and four chairs; a small garden bench by the wall; and two deckchairs. In one sits* MR GRIMSHAW, *asleep under a newspaper. In the other sits* MRS GRIMSHAW, *knitting.*

A bird is whistling almost cheekily. MR GRIMSHAW *stirs, takes up the paper and begins to read it. We have not yet seen his face. When we do, he appears, well-built middle aged, bald, and very bad-tempered of face. He is a wealthy factory owner who has 'come up the hard way'.* MRS GRIMSHAW *is also middle-aged, but is a far more 'comfortable' and sympathetic person than her husband, by whom she refuses to be bullied.*

MR GRIMSHAW: It's no good, y'know.

MRS GRIMSHAW: No, dear.

MR GRIMSHAW: We haven't been the same since the war.

MRS GRIMSHAW: No, dear.

MR GRIMSHAW: Ruined! The country's ruined!

MRS GRIMSHAW: Yes, dear.

SALLY (*off*): The red dress isn't pressed, Mum.

MRS GRIMSHAW: Then try the pink one, dear.

SALLY (*off*): But I don't like the pink one. Can't I wear my tennis shorts and a shirt?

MRS GRIMSHAW: Not today, dear. Colonel Chunter is

coming to tea and you know how old-fashioned the Chunters are.

SALLY (*Off*): But Mum . . .

MRS GRIMSHAW: Now do as you're told, dear.

SALLY (*Off*): But Mum . . .

MR GRIMSHAW (*irritably dropping the newspaper to his knees, and bellowing in the direction of Sally*): Do as your Mother says, confound you, girl!

    Pause.

She's getting as bad as the rest of her age. Contradictory. Always wanting to do different from what they're told. Look at this long-haired specimen here. Looks like an overgrown teddy-bear.

    (*Shows* MRS GRIMSHAW *the paper.*)

MRS GRIMSHAW: That's Prince Charles, dear.

MR GRIMSHAW: Is it? Oh yes, so it is. Well that's what I say. All the same. Good for nothing but hitting old women on the head and lounging about the place.

MRS GRIMSHAW: Who is, dear? Prince Charles?

MR GRIMSHAW: No. Teenagers. Teenagers today. Now in my day, you had to do as you were told, and sharp, or you were given a good beating. And that was that. Thank goodness I wasn't brought up in this modern namby-pamby way. Didn't do me a bit of harm either. I'm perfectly normal. Not twisted in any way. Am I?

MRS GRIMSHAW: No, dear.

MR GRIMSHAW: Well . . . there you are then.

    Pause.

MRS GRIMSHAW: I do wish the Chunters weren't coming to tea today. One's never quite sure about Sally's boy friends, and I've never even heard of this one.

MR GRIMSHAW: Confound it! Don't say Sally's bringing a boy friend here today!

MRS GRIMSHAW: But of course, dear. Why do you think she's so concerned about her dress? She's been talking about it since she came in for lunch.

MR GRIMSHAW: Good heavens, Milly, you don't mean we've got to put up with one of these long-haired morons half this afternoon and for tea, do you?

MRS GRIMSHAW: He may be neither long-haired nor moronic, dear. I just said I'd prefer to find out without the Chunters being here.

MR GRIMSHAW: And if she's picked him up in that café place you were soft enough to let her work in, then I suppose he'll be an out-of-work yodeller from a lemonade group.

MRS GRIMSHAW: They're called 'pop' groups, dear, and as he's only fourteen and still at school, you can hardly call him out of work.

MR GRIMSHAW: He's certainly not in work if he's still at school. They do nothing at school these days. One long holiday. Don't know what these teachers are thinking about. All we turn out now is half-baked oafs who can't spell their own names.

Enter SALLY.

SALLY: Will this do, Mum? It feels awful.

MRS GRIMSHAW: It's lovely, Sally. Very nice. Isn't it, dear?

MR GRIMSHAW: What? Oh, yes. And while you're here, missy, before you go off and change to meet this boy of yours, tell us something about him.

SALLY (*she sits at a seat by the garden table*): I already have changed, Daddy! And I've been telling you about him all through lunch.

MR GRIMSHAW: Then start again. I wasn't listening.

SALLY: But he'll be here soon, and then you can see for yourself, Daddy.

MR GRIMSHAW: Maybe. (*He crosses to* SALLY *and sits on the low garden table.*) But I'd like a bit of background information to work on, first. If you don't mind, that is. I realize, of course, that I am only your father, and have no right to meddle now you're so grown-up that you can have boy friends.

SALLY: His name is Johnny Salter, and I met him at the café this morning.

MR GRIMSHAW: Salter! Salter! Can't think of anyone by that name that we know. Can you, Milly?

MRS GRIMSHAW: I don't think we know any Salters, dear, no.

MR GRIMSHAW: Where's he from?

SALLY: He lives near the café.

MR GRIMSHAW: What! On the other side of town?

SALLY: Yes.

MR GRIMSHAW (*he storms back to his deckchair*): Good heavens, Milly, I knew it! She's picked up a savage from the slums.

SALLY: He's not a savage.

MR GRIMSHAW: He's from the other side of town. He must be. All this is the result of your letting her work in that Joe fellow's dive. Think of it! A Grimshaw wanting to marry a slum savage.

SALLY (*she rises, bursting into tears*): I don't want to marry a slum savage, I only want to go out with one.
Exit SALLY *weeping.*

MR GRIMSHAW: It's the same thing nowadays. You've neither morals nor self-respect.

MRS GRIMSHAW (*placatory*): Now, darling, don't make a scene. He's probably very nice and well brought up.

MR GRIMSHAW: And whose side are you on? Have you suddenly fallen for the primitive life as well?

MRS GRIMSHAW: Don't be silly, dear. You're quite savage enough for me. At least give the boy the benefit of the doubt, and wait until you've seen him before you decide about him.

MR GRIMSHAW: All right. Have it your own way. Let him come to tea. But don't be surprised if he not only elopes with your daughter but carries away half your jewellery as well.

MRS GRIMSHAW: You've no reason at all for thinking he's a thief, Herbert.

MR GRIMSHAW: He'll be just like that lot that work for me. Wouldn't be surprised if his father isn't one of 'em. Lazy, thieving lot. Someone is stealing all that stuff out of the warehouse. I didn't dream it up, you know.

MRS GRIMSHAW: I know, dear. But why blame the men?

MR GRIMSHAW: Who else can it be? The police can't find out. *Must* be an inside job. The windows are too small for men to get through, and the doors haven't been touched. Must be the men. I wouldn't mind having a considerable bet on it being the night-watchman.

MRS GRIMSHAW: Mr Moggs? But he's so nice, Herbert. Surely not?

MR GRIMSHAW: That's just the type who do these

things. Smarmy to your face and as cunning as a serpent behind your back. But I'll catch him, you'll see.

A door-bell rings.

SALLY (*off*): That'll be Johnny, Mum. I'll go.

MRS GRIMSHAW: Now remember, Herbert. Give him a chance.

MR GRIMSHAW: If he's a savage I shall give him a club!

Enter SALLY and JOHNNY. JOHNNY is very nervous and watches SALLY carefully for directions as to what to do and say. He makes a brave effort to be polite and correct.

SALLY: Daddy, this is Johnny Salter.

JOHNNY: Hello, sir. It's kind of you to allow me to come to tea.

GRIMSHAW *looks him up and down contemptuously.*

MR GRIMSHAW: Oh. Hello, young man. Ah! Yes, not at all. (*Returning to his paper in disgust.*) Delighted.

MRS GRIMSHAW: I'm Mrs Grimshaw, Johnny. Sally's Mother. How-do-you-do?

JOHNNY: Very well, thank you, Mrs Grimshaw.

MRS GRIMSHAW (*to MR GRIMSHAW*): Would you like your club, dear?

MR GRIMSHAW: Eh?

MRS GRIMSHAW: Sit down, Johnny. (*Indicates seat.*)

JOHNNY: Thanks.

MR GRIMSHAW (*reluctantly doing what he considers his duty*): Sally tells me you want to take her to a youth club tonight.

JOHNNY: Yes, sir. If you'll let me.

MR GRIMSHAW: Don't know that I agree with youth clubs. Dens of vice most of 'em. Breeding grounds for gang warfare.

SALLY *is making elaborate signs, from behind her*
father's chair, to JOHNNY *to keep quiet.*

MRS GRIMSHAW: Perhaps. But I wouldn't say that
Johnny looked much of a savage. Would you, dear?

MR GRIMSHAW *grunts and goes back to his paper.*

MRS GRIMSHAW: We're expecting visitors, Johnny.
When they come we'll have tea.

JOHNNY *starts up, taken aback.*

JOHNNY: Visitors . . . I . . .

SALLY (*pushing him down*): It's all right. Only the
Chunters. They're quite harmless really.

Door-bell.

MRS GRIMSHAW: That'll be them. I'll go.

Exit MRS GRIMSHAW.

JOHNNY (*loud whisper*): What'll I do? Who are they?

SALLY: Just say yes and no in the right places.

There are loud greetings off. The loudest comes from a
domineering woman. A second later, enter MRS CHUNTER
followed by COL. CHUNTER *and* PENELOPE, *their*
daughter. All three are ridiculous caricatures of real people.
MRS CHUNTER *is a modern Victorian aunt: She holds*
herself in and straight, allowing only the occasional
grandiose gesture to emphasize what she says. She barks
at both her husband and her daughter, bullying them with
every word. To other people she gives huge and meaningless
smiles. She is patronizing and always 'correct'. COL.
CHUNTER *is older. He carries a walking-stick and his*
head nods constantly. It has become a reflex with him to
agree with his wife. His speech can only be described as
'strangled'. PENELOPE *is dressed in riding clothes and*
carries a crop. She simpers and giggles all the time, and
her hands and feet suggest that she suffers paroxysms which

probably result from the brow-beating her mother indulges in when she speaks to her daughter. MRS CHUNTER *sweeps across the stage, greeting* SALLY *as she does so. Her family follow in her wake, like dutiful dogs.* MRS GRIMSHAW *watches it all, mildly amused, from the garden table.*

MRS CHUNTER: . . . and there's Sally. Hello, my dear. How charming you look; so fresh. Isn't she, Hector?

COL. CHUNTER: Stunning, dear. Reminds me of . . .

MRS CHUNTER: And who is this mannikin? A new playmate? Isn't he handsome, Hector?

COL. CHUNTER: Handsome . . .

MRS CHUNTER: And what is the dear mannikin's name, Sally?

SALLY: Johnny Salter. This is Mrs Chunter, Johnny.

MRS CHUNTER: Hello, Johnny. Let me introduce you to my daughter, Penelope. I'm sure you'll get on splendidly. Won't they, Hector?

COL. CHUNTER: Splendidly . . .

MRS CHUNTER: Ah! Herbert, there you are, hiding behind your newspaper as always.

MR GRIMSHAW: Afternoon, Bella. Well?

MRS CHUNTER: Blooming, Herbert, blooming. Aren't I, Hector?

COL. CHUNTER: Yes dear, absolutely blooming . . .

MRS CHUNTER: Milly, did I tell you about the trouble at the Cartwrights . . . ?

MRS CHUNTER *crosses to* MRS GRIMSHAW, *where they stand downstage of the table, talking.* JOHNNY, SALLY *and* PENELOPE *remain upstage centre, talking.* COL. CHUNTER *comes downstage where he is joined by* GRIMSHAW. *They stand side by side, looking out into the audience. They rise up and down on their*

toes, keeping the same rhythm, like two men in front of a
fire.

COL. CHUNTER (*after a pause*): Good afternoon, Herbert.

MR GRIMSHAW: Hector.

COL. CHUNTER: Busy?

MR GRIMSHAW: So, so.

COL. CHUNTER: Know how it is.

MR GRIMSHAW: Quite.

COL. CHUNTER: Played any golf recently?

MR GRIMSHAW: None.

COL. CHUNTER: Pity. Had a splendid round yesterday.
  With Rowlinson, y'know?

MR GRIMSHAW: Ah! Yes.

COL. CHUNTER: Splendid. (*He moves towards* MRS
  CHUNTER *and begins to demonstrate the golf shot, using
  his stick as a club, and showing enthusiasm for the first
  time.*) Got to the fourth and drifted into sand, in the
  Bottoms by the trees. Only one thing for it. Chopper!
  Use me chopper.

MR GRIMSHAW: Ah, yes.

COL. CHUNTER: Never do it, Rowlinson said. Impossible
  shot. (*He is swinging his stick wider and wider. It is
  perfectly obvious that given any more thrust it will connect
  with* MRS CHUNTER'S *rear.*)

MR GRIMSHAW: Indeed?

COL. CHUNTER: Gave it a good, underhand twist.
  Y'know. Up and under. So. (*He gives the stick a great
  swing. It strikes his wife squarely on the bottom.* MRS
  CHUNTER *screams and rounds on him.*)

MRS **CHUNTER**: Hector!

COL. CHUNTER: Sorry, m'dear. Showing Herbert me
  Bottoms shot.

MRS CHUNTER (*scandalized*): Hector!

MRS GRIMSHAW: I'll get tea.

MRS CHUNTER (*recovering, flashes a gushing smile at* MRS GRIMSHAW, *as though nothing had happened*): Let me help you, Milly.

Exit MRS GRIMSHAW *and* MRS CHUNTER. *The* COLONEL *sits in the deckchair next to* GRIMSHAW, *who sat down after the fatal blow.* CHUNTER *sits there for a while looking about him, his head nodding. He is lost for something to do. At last he notices the paper, which* GRIMSHAW *is again reading held up in front of him.* CHUNTER *edges forward, peering shortsightedly at the front page. As he gets very close,* GRIMSHAW's *bad-tempered face suddenly confronts him.* CHUNTER *relaxes back into his chair. The paper goes up again, but this time held away from the* COLONEL. *After a while he tries to lean over so that he can read over* GRIMSHAW's *shoulder. Again* GRIMSHAW's *face, even more thunderous is turned to confront him. He relaxes back once more.* GRIMSHAW *turns the other way, so that the entire front of the paper is presented towards* CHUNTER. *And once more the* COLONEL *makes an effort to read, this time trying to see the back page. Slowly the paper is lowered and* CHUNTER's *head follows it down. At last a thoroughly inflamed* GRIMSHAW *thrusts the entire front page into* CHUNTER's *lap.* CHUNTER *smiles gratefully.*

COL. CHUNTER: Thanks, Herbert.

A giggle from PENELOPE, *who is talking to* SALLY *and* JOHNNY. *They move down centre.*

PENELOPE: Do you wide, Johnny?

JOHNNY: Wide?

SALLY: Ride!

JOHNNY: Oh! Ride! Yes, a fair bit.

He is finding PENELOPE *almost too amusing for comfort.*

PENELOPE: Oh! Jolly good. What have you got?

JOHNNY: Well, actually, it's a sort of cross. It began as a Raleigh and it's had some Rudge bits added.

PENELOPE: I don't think I've heard of those breeds. Where did you buy it?

JOHNNY: My Dad got the frame for my birthday second-hand from work.

SALLY: Penelope means ride horses.

JOHNNY: Horses! Sorry. Thought you meant bikes.

PENELOPE: No, silly. (*She crosses to her father.*) Daddy, he thought I meant bikes when I asked him if he rode.

COL. CHUNTER: Well, doesn't he?

PENELOPE: No, Daddy. At least, not horses.

COL. CHUNTER: What else can you ride?

PENELOPE: Bikes, Daddy.

COL. CHUNTER: Oh, yes. O'course. Should ride, boy. Good for you. Good exercise. What you need at your age. Isn't it, Herbert?

MR GRIMSHAW: Just what I was saying to Milly before you came. Too molly-coddled children are, these days.

COL. CHUNTER: What's your seat like, boy?

JOHNNY: Quite comfortable, sir, thank you.

MR GRIMSHAW: Not that seat, you fool. The Colonel means your riding seat.

JOHNNY: Er . . . My riding seat? . . . er . . . I'm not sure, sir.

COL. CHUNTER: Ought to know about your seat. Very important to have a good seat. Show him, Penelope. Demonstrate your seat.

PENELOPE: But, Daddy, I haven't a horse.

COL. CHUNTER: Good Lor', girl. Use your head.

PENELOPE: My – my head, Daddy?

COL. CHUNTER: Your head, girl. Use yer initiative. (*To* HERBERT.) No initiative, children, nowadays.

　　PENELOPE *dithers.*

COL. CHUNTER: Yer know, sometimes I wonder if yer my own daughter. (*He struggles up and goes down centre.*) Look 'ere. I'll be your horse. (*He kneels down on all fours.*) Sit on me. On my back. Now – demonstrate your seat.

　　PENELOPE *climbs on to her father's back and goes up and down in thoroughly correct horse-back fashion.*

PENELOPE: You see, Johnny. You've got to get the rhythm.

JOHNNY: I don't see.

MR GRIMSHAW: The boy's stupid!

PENELOPE: You've got to rise and fall in time with the horse as it trots along.

JOHNNY: Why?

COL. CHUNTER: What d'yer mean, why? You do. Isn't that good enough?

JOHNNY: I suppose so, sir. But cowboys don't.

　　CHUNTER *kneels up straight suddenly.* PENELOPE *is thrown completely off his back on to the ground behind.*

COL. CHUNTER: Cowboys! That's all you think about these days.

MR GRIMSHAW: Cowboys! All the fault of television. Americans, that's all cowboys are. Loud-mouthed, spineless nation.

　　PENELOPE *has recovered and got to her feet. She comes to* JOHNNY.

PENELOPE: But if you don't do it, Johnny, the horse won't go. (*She pushes her father on to all fours.*) Look. You try. (*She makes* JOHNNY *sit on her father's back.* CHUNTER *buckles with the weight.*)

COL. CHUNTER: Now, Penelope ... Wait a moment. . . .

    JOHNNY *goes up and down as though he were a cowboy chasing a herd of stampeding steer, slapping* CHUNTER'S *hindquarters and yelling cowboy-fashion. He is enjoying himself.* CHUNTER *is puffing violently.*

COL. CHUNTER: Good heavens, boy, get up. . . .

PENELOPE: That's right, isn't it, Mr Grimshaw?

MR GRIMSHAW: He's doing splendidly.

    SPARKS *and* WRIGGLES *appear, over the wall. They break into delighted laughter at the sight. They remain watching throughout the following scene.*

    Enter MRS CHUNTER *bearing a tray of tea things, followed by* MRS GRIMSHAW, *also with tray. At the sight of her husband,* MRS CHUNTER'S *face shows exaggerated horror. She walks forward and stands behind the rider and 'horse'.*

MRS CHUNTER: Hector!

    JOHNNY *lands solidly on* CHUNTER'S *back at* MRS CHUNTER'S *bellow.* CHUNTER *collapses to the ground.* JOHNNY *falls backwards and finds himself looking up at* MRS CHUNTER.

MRS CHUNTER: What *are* you doing? Get up at once!

    JOHNNY *scrambles to his feet and clears out of the way.* CHUNTER *staggers up, exhausted and is confronted by his wife.*

MRS CHUNTER: Making an exhibition of yourself! What do you think you are?

COL. CHUNTER: I'm a horse, dear!

MRS CHUNTER: My dear Hector, you need not tell us
what we already know.

CHUNTER *returns, crestfallen to the deckchair.* MRS
CHUNTER *places her tray on the table and sits at the
upstage end. Next to her is* SALLY, *and below her is*
MRS GRIMSHAW. JOHNNY *and* PENELOPE *take the
bench and place it between* COLONEL *and* MRS CHUNTER,
thus completing an arc round the stage.

MRS GRIMSHAW *pours tea for* MRS CHUNTER, *and
passes it to* SALLY.

MRS GRIMSHAW: Mrs Chunter.

SALLY (*passing the cup*): Mrs Chunter.

MRS CHUNTER: Thank you, dear.

MRS GRIMSHAW *pours a whisky and hands it to*
SALLY.

MRS GRIMSHAW: Daddy.

SALLY (*passing it to* MR GRIMSHAW): Daddy!

*This sort of thing goes on until everyone has a cup of tea
and a cake.* JOHNNY *is fascinated by* CHUNTER'*s nodding
head. He becomes so engrossed that his own head begins to
nod, and he nearly spills his cup. Producer may work in as
much as his company can manage successfully of this sort
of parody of the polite tea-party.*

Until: JOHNNY *is just about to pick up his plate at the
same time as* CHUNTER *is picking up his cup from the
ground where they have both put them.*

MR GRIMSHAW (*suddenly returning to the former conversation*): Now, young Salter!

JOHNNY *is so taken aback that he knocks* CHUNTER'*s
cup into the air.*

MRS GRIMSHAW (*rushing to his aid*): Give it to me,
Johnny. (*Takes cup.*)

COL. CHUNTER: The boy's a fool.

JOHNNY *is very apologetic.*

MR GRIMSHAW (*when everyone is settled again*): *You* want to take *my* daughter to a club, or something? That so?

JOHNNY: Yes, Mr Grimshaw, if I may.

MR GRIMSHAW: Don't know that I like clubs. What sort is it?

JOHNNY: Just a youth club, sir. We go every Saturday. We're doing a show for Christmas.

MRS CHUNTER: A show. How thrilling. Penelope loves acting. Don't you, dear? She'd love to come, I'm sure. Wouldn't you, dear?

JOHNNY *looks sick.*

MRS CHUNTER (*to* MRS GRIMSHAW:) We've been sending her to learn singing you know. She's so talented. Aren't you, dear?

PENELOPE: Oh, Mummy! Not really. I don't think . . .

MRS CHUNTER: Don't be so modest, dear. I've told you before. You really must learn more confidence. Mustn't she, Hector?

COL. CHUNTER: More confidence . . .

MRS CHUNTER: Everyone would love to hear you sing that lovely song you were learning.

PENELOPE: But, Mummy . . .

MRS CHUNTER: Wouldn't you, Milly?

MRS GRIMSHAW: It would be charming, I'm sure.

MRS CHUNTER: Come along, Penelope.

PENELOPE: But, Mummy, I don't know it yet.

MRS CHUNTER: Or course you do, child. I heard you singing it beautifully in your bath last night. You'd love to hear it wouldn't you, Jonathan?

JOHNNY: What? Oh . . . Yes!

PENELOPE: But, Mummy. . . .

MRS CHUNTER: There we are. We're all ready.

GRIMSHAW *returns, raising his eyes heavenwards, to his paper.* PENELOPE *stands, writhing in confusion and not sure what to do with her plate.*

MRS CHUNTER *snatches it away and puts it down on the bench.*

PENELOPE (*announcing as though at a concert, but in a voice that suggests that she is only performing because she has to*): I'd like to sing for you 'Horsey, Horsey' (*she sings the chorus of 'Horsey, Horsey' published by the Sun Music Publishing Co. Ltd., in a thoroughly unmusical way. Any song that fits the scene may be used.*)

At the end, MRS CHUNTER *claps enthusiastically and far more than is necessary. Everyone else is polite, except* GRIMSHAW *who remains behind his newspaper.* PENELOPE *simpers, giggles, and sits down on the plate. She rises, horrified.* MRS CHUNTER *is disgusted, picks up the plate and hands it to* PENELOPE, *who sits in disgrace.*

GRIMSHAW *slowly lowers his paper.*

MR GRIMSHAW: Is that the sort of stuff you're doing, boy?

JOHNNY: Not quite, Mr Grimshaw. Ours is a sort of pantomime. *Cinderella.*

MR GRIMSHAW: None of this TV violence, I hope?

SALLY: Is it a real pantomime, with a dame and custard tarts and all?

JOHNNY: Yes. Everything. The club leader is the dame.

MRS CHUNTER: And have you a part, young mannikin?

JOHNNY: Yes. I'm Buttons.

MRS CHUNTER: You ought to try Penelope for Cinderella. Don't you think she'd play it beautifully? And sing so well too.

JOHNNY: Well, actually, I thought Sally might try for that. But we still need someone to be one of the ugly sisters.

GRIMSHAW *is taking a drink of whisky. He blurts it out and coughs violently.*

MRS CHUNTER: I don't think I could let our Penelope be an ugly sister. Not her at all.

SALLY: I've always wanted to know how they do a custard tart. Do tell us.

JOHNNY: It's simple really. You just have a tart made from meringue. Least that's what we do. Like this one really. (*He picks up a tart from the tray.*) Then you push it into the actor's face.

MRS GRIMSHAW: That must be fun.

JOHNNY: It is, Mrs Grimshaw. Last year the dame went chasing round the stage after the villain, and tripped up, and instead of hitting the villain, the tart went straight into the face of the vicar sitting in the front row of the audience.

They all laugh.

MR GRIMSHAW (*sourly*): Look here, boy. Instead of waving that thing about, bring the soda water.

JOHNNY: Yes, sir. (*He puts down the tart and picks up the soda siphon. It is obvious that he has never handled one before. As he crosses to* GRIMSHAW, WRIGGLES *stands up on the wall.*)

WRIGGLES (*just as* JOHNNY *is aiming at Grimshaw's glass*): Johnny!

JOHNNY *turns in surprise towards* WRIGGLES. *The soda water spurts over* CHUNTER, *who jumps away with a shout.* GRIMSHAW *shouts a warning, but only succeeds in attracting* JOHNNY'S *attention, and the direction of the soda water on to himself. Everyone stands and shouts.* WRIGGLES *dives over the wall and he and* SPARKS *disappear.* GRIMSHAW *grabs at* JOHNNY *and drives him across the stage, bellowing in anger.*

MR GRIMSHAW: Get him out of here! The boy is a savage. Unmannered, moronic. Take my daughter out! Never! I wouldn't let him take a dog for a walk.

MRS GRIMSHAW: But, Herbert, it was only an accident. Don't worry, Johnny.

Exit JOHNNY, *followed by* GRIMSHAW, *and* MRS GRIMSHAW.

MRS CHUNTER: Come along, Hector, I think it's time we left. Penelope, come.

PENELOPE: But, Mummy. . . .

MRS CHUNTER: Penelope! . . . (*Exit* MRS CHUNTER *and the* COLONEL. PENELOPE *stuffs the last of her cake into her mouth and exits.*)

SALLY: Daddy, he didn't mean it. Oh, Johnny. . . . SALLY *bursts into tears and flops down on the bench. After a moment* JOHNNY'S *head appears over the wall. He climbs into the garden, checks that the coast is clear and then sits astride the bench beside* SALLY. *He is a little embarrassed by her tears.*

JOHNNY: Don't cry.

SALLY: Johnny! How did you get in?

JOHNNY: Over the wall. I went round the side and climbed in.

SALLY: If Daddy finds you here he'll be furious.

JOHNNY: I know. But he won't come back. He's too busy cleaning himself up!

SALLY (*laughs slightly*): He was a sight, wasn't he?

They laugh together. Her laughter drains away, as she remembers that she won't be able to come to the club.

SALLY (*a threat of tears again*): Oh, Johnny. I can't come tonight.

JOHNNY: Please don't cry. Things are never as bad as they seem.

SALLY: But you don't know Daddy. If he says I can't go, he'll never change his mind.

JOHNNY (*downcast*): I'm sorry I messed things up like that.

SALLY: It wasn't your fault. It was that silly Colonel Chunter.

JOHNNY: It wasn't him really. I shouldn't have come. The others said I was wrong to come. They said I would mess things up and annoy your Dad, and they were right. I'm sorry, Sally.

SALLY: You *weren't* wrong to come. You were splendid. Mummy liked you. I could tell. She'd let me go I know. (*Pause.*) And I like you too.

JOHNNY jumps up and glares straight ahead, scared stiff.

SALLY: Really I do, Johnny.

JOHNNY (*very hesitant*): Do you?

SALLY: Yes, and I do so want to come to the club.

JOHNNY (*brightens*): Do you? Honest?

SALLY: Honest. But how?

JOHNNY: I dunno. Didn't you say your Mum would let you go?

SALLY: Yes.

JOHNNY: Well go and ask her.

SALLY: She'd never say yes, before she'd asked Daddy.

JOHNNY: What'll happen if you just go?

SALLY: I'd never get out of the house to find out.

JOHNNY: Crumbs! Bit difficult, isn't it? (*They sit glumly for a moment. Then* JOHNNY *has a sudden idea.*) Of course. Look, Sally, if you could get out of the house without them knowing, how long would it be before you were missed?

SALLY: Heavens! Well, Daddy has a dinner to go to tonight. Something to do with business. By the time he's cleaned himself from your soda water act, he'll probably want to get ready to go out. Mummy will have to help him because he can never get a stiff collar right by himself, and anyway she'll have to find half his clothes for him. So Mummy won't notice that I'm not around until about supper-time. Say seven o'clock. But honestly, Johnny, I could never get out without them knowing.

JOHNNY: But that's just it. I got in without being noticed, didn't I? So we could both get out the same way.

SALLY: Over the garden wall?

JOHNNY: Over the garden wall! How's that?

SALLY: It's great, Johnny, really. But I could never do it. Mummy would worry so.

JOHNNY: Oh, crumbs! But it's the only way. I told you I'd find a way, didn't I? And you said yourself your Mother would let you go if it wasn't for your Father.

SALLY: It's just that I'd rather she wasn't hurt. She'd be terribly worried.

JOHNNY: Well then, if it's only *that* you want her to know, leave her a message. Say where you are. She'd understand and then she wouldn't worry.

SALLY: Yes, I could do that. Where's some paper? (*She finds some on the table.*) Here, this will do.

JOHNNY: Here's a pencil. Now.

SALLY (*writing and reading aloud*): 'Dear Mummy. Have gone to the club with Johnny. Don't worry. And please don't tell Daddy. Love, Sally.' There.

JOHNNY: Whoopee! (*He cartwheels.*) I knew we'd find a way! Put it there where she'll find it. Now then – up you get.

> SALLY *climbs over the wall.* JOHNNY *stands on top looking off after her*

JOHNNY: You know, Sally. For a girl you're O.K.

> JOHNNY *disappears over the wall.*

CURTAIN

ACT THREE

SCENE ONE

Late evening, the same day. The Youth Club stage. The stage is bare (curtains hang knotted, perhaps. Anything which creates an atmosphere of an empty place). Light-stands are grouped in one corner. Centre only pieces of furniture: a costume skip and a small step-ladder. This area is pooled in light, as though the only illumination was from a working light above.

When the scene opens there is a pause. Then: enter SALLY. *She walks slowly across stage, looking about her curiously. A little after, enter* JOHNNY. *He saunters to the step-ladder, climbs it and sits on the top board. All the time he watches* SALLY, *gently amused at her curiosity. He waits until she reaches the Proscenium and turns towards him before he speaks.*

JOHNNY: We're in the middle of building the scenery. We rehearse with any old stuff until it's ready.

SALLY (*she sits on the skip*): Doesn't it look bare? You'd never think it would ever look like anything very exciting.

JOHNNY: It will though. Sometimes it's difficult to start acting when it's so bare, but then you get used to it and once you're going you don't notice that it's only a bare stage really.

SALLY: You like acting, don't you?

JOHNNY: Yes, a bit. It's different from just playing kids' games on the street. And the best part is on the nights when everything is exciting. We're early. The others won't come for a bit.

SALLY: That's because we came straight after tea.

JOHNNY: Could hardly do anything else, could we?

SALLY: No, I suppose not. (*A pause.* SALLY *sits very still, head bent,* JOHNNY *looks to see what is wrong.*)

JOHNNY: Are you worried about what they'll do when they find you've gone?

SALLY: Hm. A little.

JOHNNY: Wish you'd not come?

SALLY: Don't know really. I suppose something like this would have happened soon. Dad's horrid at times.

JOHNNY: Sorry.

SALLY: It's all right. (*She smiles up at him.*) And I would have come anyway. I'd have found some way of getting here. And it was exciting climbing over the wall. (*A pause.* SALLY *relaxes a little and making herself more comfortable on the skip, gazes about her.* JOHNNY *sits watching her. Their eyes meet and they smile at each other.*) Tell me what you do in the pantomime.

JOHNNY: Oh, I'm Buttons, I have to do the custard-tart thing. And I have to sing a song called 'If I ruled the World'.

SALLY: Sing a song. I'd like to hear it. Sing it for me.

JOHNNY: You'll hear it later on.

SALLY: I'd like to hear it now. Won't you? Please?

JOHNNY: O.K. When we rehearse we play the tune from a recording and sing to that. It's over there. I'll put it on. (*He goes into wings.*)

SALLY: Don't you like singing it?

JOHNNY: Not much. Like the custard tart better. (*Returns to the ladder.*)

SALLY: I hope you do the custard tart as well as you did the soda water.

JOHNNY (*laughs*): So do I. A beauty that was.

    Music: a recorded accompaniment to 'If I ruled the World'. (From PICKWICK. Published by Delfont Music.) JOHNNY *sings.*

SALLY: I like it. It's a nice song.

JOHNNY (*going to the wings to switch off the accompaniment*): I suppose it is. It's a bit sloppy. But all right.

    SALLY *gets up from the skip and walks to the front stage looking out into the auditorium, as though it were empty.*

SALLY: Isn't it funny – this empty hall and the stage? Lonely and deserted. You'd never think it could be hot and noisy and full of people.

JOHNNY (*returning from the wings, he joins* SALLY): I know. I like to come here sometimes before the others. Sometimes it's good to be alone.

SALLY: Do you think so? I'm often alone and I don't like it that much.

JOHNNY: Yes, but I'm always with Sparks and Wriggles and the others. (*As he talks he wanders to the Proscenium Arch and leans against it.*) We go to school together and we live in the same road, and we do everything together. We always have. Ever since we were allowed out alone. Sparks and me, we started school together, and went to the dentist for the first time together. We even had measles together. We caught it on the same day. And we both cried so much about not seeing each other that in the end our mothers put us in the same bed. Sparks is my best pal.

SALLY (*wandering round the ladder, and back to the skip, casually*): I've never had a best pal. There's Penelope, but she's too silly really. She's a tremendous rider, but somehow you can't really do anything else with her.

JOHNNY: That doesn't surprise me. I can do anything with Sparks. He's great. (*He returns to the ladder and, kneeling on the steps, leans against the top.*) But sometimes I just want to be on my own. Just lately, that is. I never used to. And so I come in here early. You know – at home the telly is always on, and Dad's sitting watching it. And my sister always has some friend of hers in the other room. And you can't go anywhere and be alone. Not quiet and alone. But here before the others come it's quiet, and I think of all the people who are going to be sitting out there soon, and how nervous I'll be and excited. But just then I'm not excited just quiet and I think of all the things I'd like to do, if I could.

SALLY: Like what?

JOHNNY: Hundreds of things. (*He wanders round to the other side of the skip.*) I'd like to go to the moon. Be one of the first to do it, you know, not when it's the usual thing to do for your summer holiday.

SALLY (*laughing*): Do you think it'll ever be like that?

JOHNNY: Course. Bound to be. Like flying. Once no one thought we ever would. Now hundreds of people do it just for fun.

SALLY: What else?

JOHNNY: Squirt soda water at Mrs Chunter!

SALLY: Me too. I've always wanted to do something like that to her. But what would you *really* like to do?

JOHNNY: Do you mean seriously?

SALLY: Yes, seriously.

He sits beside SALLY on the skip. He's thoughtful and very serious.

JOHNNY: I'd like to do something really well. Be an absolute expert. It must be great to be best at something. Better than anybody. To know something inside out and to be able to do it as easy as pie, no bother, just do it. It wouldn't matter to me if it was something special or just something ordinary, but whatever it is I'd like to do it best of anybody. And one day I will. (*Pause.*) Does that sound daft and bigheaded? I've never told anybody that before.

SALLY: No of course it isn't silly, and it's not bigheaded.

JOHNNY: Anyway that's what I think about when I'm here alone. And that's why I like to be alone.

SALLY: I've felt a bit like that myself. Only it's the other way with me. I get so fed-up thinking about myself. I'm on my own so much. That's why I took this job at Joe's Place really. I just long to be somewhere doing things with other people. Not people like the Chunters, but people who enjoy themselves and do things together because they want to, and not because it's the right thing to do. Like the Colonel plays golf because it's the right thing to do. Or Penelope rides because Mum thinks it's the right thing to do. Thank goodness my Mother's not like that, though Dad is a bit. Actually, though, Dad is only bothered about the business so he doesn't really care what I do.

JOHNNY: I was a bit scared of your Dad.

SALLY: There's no need to be. He can be fine when he wants to be. But he's come up the hard way and I suppose he's forgotten what it's like to be young. So he doesn't understand us. In a way, he never was young. He was working by the time he was fourteen and didn't have much money.

JOHNNY: My Dad was like that. When he talks about it, I'm glad I wasn't born then. It's much better now.

SALLY: Do you think so?

JOHNNY: Certain. Adults are all wrong when they say the world's getting a worse place to live in. Least, that's what I think.

There is a pause. Then SALLY *notices the skip she is sitting on.*

SALLY: What's this?

JOHNNY: It's called a skip. It's what costumes come in when you hire them for a play.

SALLY: Are there any clothes in it?

JOHNNY: Expect so. It's an old one we keep our rehearsal costumes in.

SALLY: Let me see. (*They open the skip and she pulls out a bridal dress.*)

SALLY: Look at this! How lovely!

JOHNNY: It's the dress Cinderella gets married in. It's an old one somebody gave us.

SALLY: I *must* try it. Will anybody mind?

JOHNNY: Doubt it. Sparks had it on last week and was mucking about in it.

SALLY: He shouldn't. It's too nice. (*She puts it on.*)

SALLY (*as she puts the dress on*): You put something on. Go on.

JOHNNY: O.K. (*He takes a topper and a tail coat. As he puts them on, the lights fade until they are spotted.*)

JOHNNY: How about that! Anybody would think we
    were posh.

She takes his arm and stands square with him.
SALLY: Or even getting married.

    JOHNNY *releases the hold and glances at her shyly.*
JOHNNY: Steady. Bit soon for that yet!
SALLY: Yes, I suppose so.
JOHNNY: Don't want to rush into these things!
SALLY: No. (*Pause.*) Will you ever, do you think?
JOHNNY: Get married? . . . Maybe . . . Don't know.

    They gaze at each other uncertainly. Then:
    *Loud clapping from the rear of the hall. The lights
suddenly return to normal.*

    BOUNCER, BIFF *and* SMIG *stride up to the stage, clap-
ping derisively all the time.* JOHNNY, *covered in confusion,
removes the topper and tails, throws them into the wings
and stands prepared for* BOUNCER *and* BIFF *who join him
by the Proscenium.* SALLY *takes off the dress and is joined
at the skip by a leering* SMIG.
JOHNNY: What do you want, Barton?
BIFF: Always friendly, is Johnny.
SMIG: You say if we're butting in, Johnny.
JOHNNY: You are!
BOUNCER: Sorry, old son. If we'd known we'd have
    gone away.
SALLY: Then go!

    BOUNCER *glances round at* SALLY. *Then in mock sur-
prise looks at* BIFF.
BOUNCER: Was that you said that, Biff?
BIFF (*picking up* BOUNCER'S *tone*): No, Bouncer. Was it
    you, Smig?
SMIG: Me? No.

BIFF: It wasn't him *or* me, Bouncer.

BOUNCER: Then it must have been this little lady here, Biff.

BIFF: Must have.

They close in round SALLY.

SALLY: I think you're horrible, Barton!

BOUNCER: Oh! Come, now. Them's not nice things to say. (*He takes* SALLY's *arm.*)

SALLY: Let me go! (*She struggles.*)

BOUNCER (*pulling her close*): Let's have fun.

JOHNNY: You heard, Barton, let her go.

BOUNCER: At a price, Salter.

JOHNNY: Look, you! I'll thump the daylights out of you if you don't lay off!

BOUNCER: You could try. Grab him, Smig, Biff!

(SMIG *and* BIFF *grab* JOHNNY *who struggles.* BOUNCER *secures his hold on* SALLY.)

You and me's going to get acquainted.

SALLY *struggles.*

JOHNNY: Lay off her, Barton. (*He struggles again.*) Let her go! You wait till I get at you, Barton. You're scared, that's all.

BIFF: Did you hear him, Bouncer? Says you're frightened.

JOHNNY: So he is! The only way he wins is by dirty yellow tricks.

BOUNCER: O.K. So maybe I don't fight fair. But why should I? I've never met anyone in this lousy world who *is* fair. Why should I fight fair?

JOHNNY: Try doing it for once and see.

BOUNCER: Look, Salter. You and me have it coming, see? Let's work it out once and for all. You don't like

me, and I don't like you. And you say I don't fight
fair. O.K. How about this: I'll bet you daren't get into
old Grimshaw's warehouse tonight and fetch something out that'll prove you've been in. Oh – nothing
valuable. Nothing to worry about. A bit of paper with
the firm's name on maybe. Just to show you've been
in. What about it?

JOHNNY: What for?

BOUNCER: What for? To keep us off your girl. That's
what for.

BIFF: And to prove you aren't a coward.

JOHNNY: I'm no coward and you know it!

BOUNCER: Then prove it.

BIFF: Yeah – prove it.

SMIG: Or are you scared?

  Pause.

JOHNNY: O.K.

SALLY: No, Johnny, you mustn't.

BOUNCER: Shake.

  They shake hands.

BOUNCER: See you here at ten, Salter. Come on,
Biff.

  Exit BOUNCER, BIFF *and* SMIG, *running through the
  auditorium. They laugh raucously.* JOHNNY *stays by the
  ladder.* SALLY *stands by the skip.*

SALLY: Johnny, you can't go.

JOHNNY: I've got to. Can't you see. You're just like
Sparks. You think it doesn't matter about these things,
but it does.

SALLY: But why do *that*? Why go into the warehouse?
It's dangerous.

JOHNNY: Cos they suggested it. That's why. And

what's being dangerous got to do with it? Lots of things are dangerous.

SALLY: But the police are watching the warehouse, Johnny. They might catch you.

JOHNNY: Hard luck! It won't take long. Only a minute or two. And I'm only taking something small, like a letter or something. Nothing that would be pinching really.

SALLY: But if they catch you?

JOHNNY: They won't! They won't catch me. Honest. Don't worry. It'll be all right.

SPARKS *enters very gay.*

SPARKS: Hello, Johnny! (*He sees* SALLY.) Crumbs you got her here!

JOHNNY (*flatly*): Hello, Sparks.

SPARKS: Sorry I spoke. What's up? Thought you'd be happy if you got Sally here.

JOHNNY: Oh, shut up!

Exit JOHNNY.

SPARKS: What's up with him?

SALLY: He's just made a dare with Bouncer Barton.

SPARKS: With *Barton*! Now what?

SALLY: Barton got Johnny annoyed and now he's said he'll go into my Dad's warehouse and take something to prove he is not a coward.

SPARKS: Oh no! The idiot. When?

SALLY: Tonight.

SPARKS: We'll have to stop it.

SALLY: I know, but how?

SPARKS: Dunno. We'll just have to keep an eye on him and watch out for him leaving the club. If we both do it, one of us ought to notice.

Enter CARROTS. *She has changed into a dress and looks pretty, almost 'slinky'.*

CARROTS: Hello, Sparks. (*With mock politeness.*) Hello, Sally.

SALLY: Hello.

SPARKS *stands aghast and stares.*

CARROTS: You seeing a vision, Sparks?

SPARKS: You sure you're Carrots?

CARROTS: Jane Marigold Cartwright, better known as Carrots. Uh-huh!

SPARKS: Crumbs! (*He approaches her hesitantly but grinning widely.*) You know, Carrots, sometimes I think I've misjudged you!

CARROTS (*innocently*): Oh?

SPARKS: You know how it is? When you're around with someone a lot, well . . . you take them for granted. You know?

CARROTS: I *think* so.

SPARKS: And you know, I think I've been taking you for granted too long?

CARROTS: Oh! Sparks! How nice . . .

SPARKS: Yeah. Well . . . would you like a coke?

CARROTS: Love one.

SPARKS: Let's go! (*He takes her hand.*)

CARROTS (*woman to woman*): Bye, Sally.

SPARKS: Oh yeah – see yer, Sally. Oh! Don't forget – keep your eyes skinned!

SALLY *nods. Exit* SPARKS *giving* CARROTS *an almost cave-man pull.*

SPARKS (*Off*): Watcher, Johnny.

Enter JOHNNY. ***He*** *leans against the ladder. He's worried and is trying not to show it.*

JOHNNY (*flatly*): Sparks seemed gay.

SALLY: Mmm. I think he's just noticed Carrots.

JOHNNY: Yes. I saw she'd changed! (*He tries to raise a smile but can't. They look at each other.*)

SALLY: Johnny, don't go.

JOHNNY (*gently*): Got to . . . honest. Some things you've just *got* to do. (*He gets up and holds out a hand to her.*)

JOHNNY: Look. I'll buy you a coke. Eh?

    SALLY *looks at him. She rises and takes his hand.*

SALLY: Yes please.

    They exit together.

CURTAIN

SCENE TWO

On the apron, in front of the main curtain: light as though from a street lamp. It is very late the same Saturday Thunder rolls in the distance.

The POLICEMAN *comes through the auditorium, flashing his torch about, checking his beat is secure. He mounts the apron and exits by the Proscenium.*

A moment after he has gone, BOUNCER *and* JOHNNY *appear, furtively. They are on their way to the warehouse. They pause in the light from the street lamp.*

BOUNCER: Sure you still want to go through with it, Salter?

JOHNNY: Yes. Don't you worry about me.

BOUNCER: I'm not worried about you, Johnny, boy. I just don't want you to get into hot water for nothing.

JOHNNY: I won't get into hot water. And anyhow, we're not doing anything that bad.

BOUNCER: That's right, Johnny. We're not doing anything *that* bad. Remember: watch for the night-watchman, and you fetch anything small enough to carry what has Grimshaw's name on it. O.K.?

JOHNNY: O.K. What are you going to do?

BOUNCER: Oh . . . I'll be waiting outside for you. Come on. The window we get in through is just along here.

Exit JOHNNY *and* BOUNCER. *Thunder rolls nearer.* SALLY *appears, following* JOHNNY *and* BOUNCER, *and exits after them. After a moment* BIFF *and* SMIG *appear and stop in the street light.*

BIFF: They should be in there now. Give him ten minutes, Bouncer said, didn't he, Smig?

SMIG: Yeah. Ten minutes. They've had all of that now. You remember what Bouncer said to do?

BIFF: Yeah. Come along after about ten minutes, he said, and climb in and wait until the lights go on and then grab Salter. That's what he said.

SMIG: And then we can make sure of him before we ring the police.

BIFF: Yeah.

There is a flash of lightning and a great roll of thunder.

SMIG: Crumbs! Come on, Biff, before we get wet. Just as well we're going inside.

Exit BIFF *and* SMIG. *As they go* SPARKS *and* CARROTS *appear. They have been following* BIFF *and* SMIG *and have overheard their conversation.*

SPARKS: Crikey, Carrots, did you hear that? They are gonna trap Johnny. I knew there was something fishy about that dare! Barton wouldn't have done anything like that unless there was something queer about it.

CARROTS: We've got to do something, Sparks, and quick. We've got to get Johnny out of there before the police arrive. What'll we do?

SPARKS: There's only one thing we can do. You go off and round up the gang and any other kids you see that don't like Bouncer. And you get them here just as fast as you can.

CARROTS: All right. But what are you going to do?

SPARKS: Me? I'm going in after them lot. Johnny'll never cope on his own, not with three of them, but two of us might stand a chance until you get the gang here.

CARROTS: But, Sparks, you can't. You might get copped too.

SPARKS: Shut up, and get cracking! If you hadn't changed into that dress tonight you might have been able to run faster. Now, GO ON!

CARROTS: Remind me to hate you when tonight's over!

Exit CARROTS, *the way she came. Exit* SPARKS, *following the others.*

Darkness. Then another flash of lightning and a roll of thunder. The front curtains have opened, and now the lights come up to reveal the inside of the warehouse. There are bales and boxes stacked. An old table is up centre, with an electric light hanging above it. On the table is Moggs's sandwich tin, a torch, a box of matches, some note-paper. MOGGS *sits at the table reading a newspaper and whistling softly a tuneless song. After a moment,* JOHNNY's *head appears round a bale behind* MOGGS. MOGGS *puts the paper down and stretches lazily.* JOHNNY's *head disappears.* MOGGS *looks at his watch.*

MOGGS: Time for a cuppa! (*He gets up, picks up a kettle from under the table and exits downstage.* JOHNNY's *head reappears. He checks that the coast is clear then tiptoes out and begins to search about among the things on the table.*)

MOGGS (*Off*): Where'd I put those matches?

JOHNNY *starts in surprise and runs behind a bale. Enter* MOGGS. *He goes to the table, finds the matches and exits again.* JOHNNY *returns to the search. At last he finds a piece of note-paper, which he puts into his pocket. He is just about to exit when all the lights go off. There is complete darkness.*

MOGGS (*Off*): What the . . . ? Must be the fuses!

Suddenly MOGG's *torch stabs through the darkness and at once there is another flash of lightning and roll of thunder.* JOHNNY *is seen, standing like a startled animal, exactly where he was when the lights went off.* MOGGS *has seen him in the lightning flash and trains the torch-beam on to him.* MOGGS *rushes across and drives* JOHNNY *against the Proscenium Arch, shining the beam into* JOHNNY's *face.*

MOGGS: Stand where you are. D'you hear? Good heavens! Johnny! Whatever do you think you're on at, lad?

JOHNNY (*stubborn and afraid*): Nothing!

MOGGS: Now look, son, I don't mind a joke, if I know what I'm laughing about. But this hardly seems very funny.

JOHNNY: I just had a dare, that's all.

MOGGS: Dare? Who with?

JOHNNY: With another boy.

MOGGS: What about?

JOHNNY: Nothing!

MOGGS: Now look, lad. Dare or no dare, friend or no friend, you didn't ought to come creeping in here at night and taking stuff. It's wrong, see? And it might be dangerous. I might have clobbered you one that would have put paid to you for good.

JOHNNY: All right. I'm sorry.

MOGGS: That's all very well. But you ought to have thought before you come in. Daft place to pick on anyway with it being burgled so much.

JOHNNY (*startled*): Burgled? When?

MOGGS: Didn't you know? You must be the only one in town who doesn't. Regular as clockwork, every week. And nobody knows how it's done, or who it is. Blaming me they are.

JOHNNY: You, Moggy! But you wouldn't do a thing like that.

MOGGS: I know that. And you know that. But you try telling Mr Grimshaw that.

JOHNNY: Him! I've seen enough of him for a bit, I can tell you.

MOGGS: Party a flop, eh?

JOHNNY: A complete mess.

MOGGS: Sorry. But who's this pal of yours you been having a dare with?

JOHNNY: Pal! He's no pal. It's . . .

A sudden flash of lightning again. In the flash, BOUNCER *is seen coming up behind* MOGGS *about to cosh him. We just see him do it. Then darkness as* MOGGS *crumples to the floor.*

Silence a moment. Then:

BOUNCER: All right, Biff. Put the lights on.

> *The lights come on.* BOUNCER *stands calmly swinging a huge spanner.*

JOHNNY: You!

BOUNCER: Who else?

JOHNNY: What are you doing here?

BOUNCER: Just looking after you, Johnny, pal. That's all.

JOHNNY: What did you do that for?

BOUNCER: As I say: looking after you.

> JOHNNY *kneels down at* MOGGS's *side and looks closely at him.*

JOHNNY: Now we're for it. He's out cold.

BOUNCER: So? (BOUNCER *goes to the table and sits in the chair.* JOHNNY *stands over him.*)

JOHNNY: You're a stupid idiot, Barton. There was no call to hit Moggy. He'd have let me go.

BOUNCER: That's what I was afraid of, Johnny, old pal.

JOHNNY: How do you mean?

BOUNCER: You ain't going to get let go. Didn't you hear what the man said? The police are watching this place for burglars. Well, Johnny. You've been burgling.

JOHNNY: You've gone mad. I came in cos you dared me. I only took this scrap of paper with Grimshaw's name on it. That's not burgling.

BOUNCER: You tell that to the copper, mate.

JOHNNY: Which copper? There isn't any copper here.

BOUNCER: You know, you're thick, Salter! There ain't no copper *yet*, but there's going to be soon.

JOHNNY: Going to be soon? How do you know?

BOUNCER: Cos we'll tell him to come. Biff and Smig and me.

JOHNNY: What!

BOUNCER: Getting the idea at last, boy?

JOHNNY: You mean, you'll try to have me caught in here by a copper?

BOUNCER: That's it, professor.

JOHNNY: What for?

BOUNCER: What for! (*He suddenly laughs heartily.*) For fun, Salter, for fun. Thought you'd won this morning, didn't you? Thought you'd got one over poor Bouncer. Well, settle this little packet, boyo. You heard what Moggs said. About the burglars what they can't catch. Me − that's standing in front of you, mate. That's who the burglar is. And I'm not going to be caught − you are. I've more to do than be copped by bobbies. Chased by them all my life I have. Kicked from pillar to post by rotten snobs who couldn't care a damn! That's been me, ever since my Dad died. Well I'll show them they can't meddle with me no more.

JOHNNY: So you're going to fix this burglary on me?

BOUNCER: Right first time.

JOHNNY: It'll never stick!

BOUNCER: We'll see.

JOHNNY: What about Moggy. He might die if he's left there.

BOUNCER (*spits*): Let him rot.

> JOHNNY *suddenly attacks* BOUNCER *and drives him against the bales, pinning him down.*

JOHNNY: You're a right swine, Barton! There's no other word. This has gone far enough. We're ringing for an ambulance, and the police. And when they get here you can tell your tale to them.

BOUNCER: Who says?

JOHNNY: I say.

BOUNCER: You and who's army? (*They struggle.*
  BOUNCER *is getting the worst of it.*)
BOUNCER: BIFF! SMIG!

  Enter BIFF, *and* SMIG, *who has* SALLY *held by the
  arms.* BIFF *helps* BOUNCER *to overcome* JOHNNY, *whom
  they pull to his feet and hold between them.*

BIFF (*indicating* SALLY): Look what we found, Bouncer!
BOUNCER: Well, well!
SMIG: She was hiding behind them bales and listening.
BOUNCER: Was she now?
JOHNNY (*struggling*): Leave her alone!
SMIG: Shurrup, Salter. (*He gags* JOHNNY.)
BIFF: What do we do with her, Bouncer?
BOUNCER: Let's leave them together, eh? I mean, they're
  gone on each other. They'd love to be together.
SMIG: What about the coppers?
BOUNCER: Well, what could be better? Our old pal
  Johnny and his girl friend who just happens to be the
  owner's daughter! And her not supposed to be with
  him! Coppers'll love it.
BIFF: Then come on. Or they'll be picking us up an' all.

  They bring JOHNNY *and* SALLY *together, both
  struggling. As they do so there is a Tarzan-like cry from
  above and* SPARKS *comes swinging on a rope down on to
  them, scattering them all. There is a fight.* SALLY *gets free.*

JOHNNY (*from the scrum*): Get the police, Sally, quick!

  MOGGS *begins to come round. There is a yell from*
  PUFF *as he enters followed by* NYLON, CARROTS *and*
  WRIGGLES.

PUFF: Come on, you lot.

  The gang charge into the fight and soon have BOUNCER
  and gang pinned down.

JOHNNY: Come on, sit on them! Sit on him, Wriggles! And you, Puff.

The three toughs are pulled into a line, heads facing downstage. WRIGGLES *and* PUFF *each sit on* BIFF *and* SMIG. CARROTS *sits on* BOUNCER. NYLON *mutters things about his pullover, which he brushes down, as he stands above the bodies.* JOHNNY *and* SPARKS *go to* MOGGS's *aid.*

JOHNNY: Moggs!

MOGGS: What hit me?

JOHNNY: Bouncer Barton.

MOGGS: What's he doing here!

SPARKS: He's trying to make it look like Johnny is the burglar, that's what.

MOGGS: Whatever for?

JOHNNY: Cos he's the real burglar, that's what for.

MOGGS: Him! How d'you know? My head . . . ! (*He gets up and staggers to the seat at the table.*)

JOHNNY: Cos he told me just now. Are you O.K., Mr Moggs?

MOGGS: Yes, son, I'm all right. Don't you worry about me. But what about your pals here? What have you done about them?

WRIGGLES: We're sitting on them, Mr Moggs. At least Puff is. And that's enough to keep anybody down.

PUFF: Cheek!

NYLON: My pullover's got all crumpled in that dust-up. I don't know what my Mother will say!

CARROTS: You know, boys are very soft to sit on really. This one is anyhow. You can bounce up and down on him like a mattress. Look. No wonder he's called Bouncer. (*She bounces up and down on* BOUNCER.)

SPARKS: You want to practise getting your seat right Johnny!

MOGGS: Now look here, you lot. What have you done about this mouldy crew?

JOHNNY: Sally's gone off for the police. She should be back soon.

WRIGGLES: Will they believe what happened, Johnny?

JOHNNY: Crikey, Wriggles, they'd better. Anyway Sparks heard it all.

SPARKS: Yeah. I saw what was happening as soon as I got in through the window. And I remembered that film on the telly the other night where the cop climbed up a warehouse rope . . .

PUFF: Yeah, I saw that. Or some of it. Then my Dad wanted the wrestling, blow him! It wasn't half good . . .

SPARKS: . . . and I thought, this is a warehouse and ought to have ropes. And I climbed up the ladder on to the catwalk that runs round the walls all round and found a rope that hung down just over here, and I heard what they was saying all the time cos the place was so quiet, and then when I saw they was going to put Johnny where the police could find them, I swung down and joined the party.

WRIGGLES: Lummy, Sparks. You wasn't half brave!

SPARKS: Wasn't anything, Wriggles, really. You would have done the same.

WRIGGLES: Would I, Sparks? *Crumbs!*

CARROTS: Proper little Tarzan is our Sparks!

JOHNNY: Yeah. But it means there's more than one telling the same story, doesn't it, so the police have just got to believe us.

WRIGGLES: Yes, Johnny. But there's (*he counts*) *three* of them.

SPARKS: He's right, Johnny! There's three of Bouncer's lot to say we're not telling the truth!

SALLY (*Off*): They're through here.

MOGGS: Well, lad, we shall soon see who they believe because they're here.

Enter SALLY *and* POLICEMAN.

SALLY: Here they are, Officer.

POLICEMAN: Nice little party going on here then. Evening, Mr Moggs. Trouble?

JOHNNY and SPARKS (*together*): It's like this/It's not trouble really/Johnny was dared to come in by Barton It was only a joke really/But Barton knocked Moggy out/They were trying to frame Johnny/We didn't mean any harm.

POLICEMAN: Stop! Stop the mighty roar of London's traffic and talk one at a time. (*He crosses to the bodies.*) And what are you three sitting on those boys for?

CARROTS: We're playing at bed-sitters, sir.

POLICEMAN: And what game is that?

CARROTS: You see, sir: they are the beds and we are the sitters.

POLICEMAN: Now look here! We'll have sensible talk, or else I'll run the lot of you in and you can talk to the Sergeant.

JOHNNY: Well, you see, Constable . . .

POLICEMAN: Just wait one minute, lad. One minute while I get my note-book out. (*He takes out his note-book in elaborate style, then his pencil, licks the end, and prepares to write.*)
Now then . . .

JOHNNY: I was dared to come in here and take something to prove I'd been. I climbed in through the
lavatory window in the men's washroom and had just
taken this piece of paper with the factory name on it
when Mr Moggs caught me. And then Barton coshed
him and Barton's gang came and we had a scrap. And
then you came.

POLICEMAN: What were you dared for?

JOHNNY: Nothing really . . . just a dare.

POLICEMAN: Uh-huh! (*He turns to the bodies on the floor.*)
Hey – you!

 BARTON *suddenly with a great shove, pushes* CARROTS
off, so that she sprawls on the floor. He gets up.

BOUNCER: Me, sir?

POLICEMAN: Yes, you.

CARROTS: Pity. He was so nice: like a big fat cushion.

POLICEMAN: Is what he says true?

BOUNCER: What Salter says?

POLICEMAN: Yes.

BOUNCER: No. Not anywhere near. All lies.

 Outbursts from JOHNNY *and gang, silenced by the*
POLICEMAN.

POLICEMAN: Then let's hear your story.

BOUNCER: This ain't no story, Constable, honest. This
is what happened. You know? What really happened.
And my pals what saw it will be witnesses. Won't you?

BIFF and SMIG: Yes – witnesses – that's what we is.

POLICEMAN: Come on. Let's have it.

BOUNCER: Well we sees Salter leaving the club tonight
with his girl . . .

JOHNNY: She's not my girl . . .

POLICEMAN: Quiet, lad. You've had your turn.

JOHNNY: But . . .

POLICEMAN: Quiet! (*To* BOUNCER.) Go on.

BOUNCER: We sees him leave the club and we hears him
  say they was going to climb in somewhere, but we
  didn't hear where. Did we, boys?

BIFF: No.

SMIG: No. No, we didn't.

BOUNCER: So I says: Follow them. Follow them, I says,
  and see what they're up to. So we did. Didn't we?

BIFF: Yes.

SMIG: Yes, yes we did.

BOUNCER: And we sees them climb in here just like he
  says and so we follows them. Can't be up to any good,
  I says. We'll cop them, I says, and then hand them to
  the police cos that's our duty. Didn't I?

BIFF: Yes.

SMIG: Yes, yes you did.

BOUNCER: And that's what we would have done, if
  them others of Salter's gang hadn't come along and
  out-numbered us. Wouldn't we?

BIFF: Yes.

SMIG: Yes, yes we would.

  *There is uproar. The gangs shout back and forth at each
  other. The* POLICEMAN *and* MOGGS *hold them off and
  try to quieten them. Enter* GRIMSHAW *and* MRS GRIM-
  SHAW.

MR GRIMSHAW (*shouting*): QUIET!

  There is instant silence and they look aghast at GRIM-
  SHAW.

MR GRIMSHAW: What's going on, Officer?

POLICEMAN: I was taking a statement, sir, about these
  people who were caught in your works.

MR GRIMSHAW: Able to take ten statements at once, are you?

POLICEMAN: No, sir. You see the two lads here are disagreeing and they started a row just as you came in, sir.

MR GRIMSHAW: I see. Sally, I'll talk to you later.

MRS GRIMSHAW *takes her protectively.*

MRS GRIMSHAW: Don't worry, dear. We found your note and went to the police station, and just as we got there a policeman told us there had been a break-in at the warehouse so we came straight here.

MR GRIMSHAW: Quiet, Milly. We'll deal with her later. (*To the* POLICEMAN.) So they are disagreeing, are they?

POLICEMAN: Yes, sir.

MR GRIMSHAW: Don't you know what happened, Moggs? Weren't you here?

MOGGS: Yes, Mr Grimshaw. But I was knocked out and don't know everything that went on. It seems these lads came in for a dare, but young Barton, here, denies it. Says Salter was intending to steal stuff. Salter says it's the other way about and that Barton's been burgling the place.

MR GRIMSHAW: Which is Barton?

BOUNCER (*arrogantly*): Me, Mr Grimshaw. Me – I'm Barton.

MR GRIMSHAW: You're cocky too. However, we'll soon see who's right.

BOUNCER: How do you mean?

MR GRIMSHAW: It so happens, Barton, that this place has been burgled regularly for a number of weeks.

BOUNCER (*carelessly*): Has it?

MR GRIMSHAW: It has. And that's a fact Salter seems to know already!

JOHNNY: But I . . .

MR GRIMSHAW (*to* JOHNNY): Don't bother. (*To* BOUNCER.) As we couldn't think how it was being done, nor catch anybody at it, I had to think up a little trick to help.

BOUNCER (*startled*): Trick?

MR GRIMSHAW: Yes, trick, Barton, lad. In the shape of a machine called a tape-recorder. It's hidden in the office at the back, and the microphone is hidden just up there above Mr Moggs's desk.

The gangs murmur and gaze up at the ceiling.

MOGGS: Above my desk?

MR GRIMSHAW: Above your desk, Moggs. I'm sorry to say I suspected you, and wanted proof.

MOGGS: That was a bit off, Mr Grimshaw, if I might say so.

MR GRIMSHAW: Maybe, Moggs. But it might also be the solution to the little argument that was running here a minute or two ago. Now, if you'll all just wait here a moment, I'll be back with the magic box.

Exit MR GRIMSHAW. *They all look round at one another, puzzled. They can't understand. Mutterings ad lib.* MR GRIMSHAW *returns bearing a portable tape-recorder. They gather round in a bunch quiet and wondering.*

MR GRIMSHAW: Here we are. How long ago is it since you were attacked, Moggs?

MOGGS: About quarter of an hour ago, sir.

MR GRIMSHAW: Good. That was just about the time the machine was set to start. Let's see if we can judge the point on the tape that recorded what was going on a quarter of an hour ago.

MR GRIMSHAW *has rewound the tape to the point where the following is heard . . .*

'JOHNNY: *You mean you'll try to have me caught in here by a copper?' to* 'JOHNNY: . . . *And when they come you can tell your tale to them.*'

MR GRIMSHAW (*switching off*): Seems pretty conclusive, Barton.

There is a pause. BOUNCER *suddenly pushes* BIFF *into* SMIG *who falls against the* POLICEMAN. BOUNCER *rushes for the door, but* JOHNNY *has anticipated him. He bounds after* BOUNCER, *and brings him down with a rugger tackle. There is a scuffle, which ends with* JOHNNY *triumphant on top of* BARTON, *and the* POLICEMAN *taking charge of* BOUNCER. *General uproar.*

In the skirmish, PUFF *has grabbed* BIFF *and* NYLON *has grabbed* SMIG, *whom they hold on either side of the* POLICEMAN *and* BOUNCER.

POLICEMAN (*picking up* BARTON): All right, lad. That'll do. You can come with me to the station.

JOHNNY (*to* MR GRIMSHAW): I'm sorry I broke in, Mr Grimshaw. I can see it was a daft thing to do, but I was dared, and sometimes you just *have* to do a dare. Haven't you, Sparks?

SPARKS: Yes, you have. He just *had* to do Barton's dare, Mr Grimshaw. He couldn't have looked us in the face again if he hadn't.

JOHNNY: And I'm sorry about taking Sally to the club. It was my fault, all of it. I persuaded her. She didn't want to come really, not without your say-so.

MRS GRIMSHAW: Now isn't that nice, Herbert? You see, I told you you wouldn't need your club.

MR GRIMSHAW: All right, Milly. You win. I can see

what you were up to. And it's all ended happily. So let's forget it, eh?

POLICEMAN: Mr Moggs, you'd better come to the station as well.

MOGGS: What about the warehouse? Can't leave that.

JOHNNY: It's all right, Moggs. We'll stay till you can get back. Won't we, Sparks?

SPARKS: Yes, we'll stay.

MOGGS: Well . . . I don't know . . .

MR GRIMSHAW: Come, come, Moggs. Time we trusted the younger generation, you know. Always said they had plenty of good in them.

MOGGS: Well, sir . . . if you say so.

MR GRIMSHAW: We'll send a relief up from the station. I'll need the tape-recorder. Milly, you'd better take Sally home.

SALLY: Can't I stay too Daddy, until the relief comes?

MR GRIMSHAW: A bit late. I . . .

MRS GRIMSHAW: Oh, Herbert. After such a time! They could ring us from here when the new man comes and we could pick them up in the car.

MR GRIMSHAW: Suppose so. Yes. We'll pick you up. Give us a ring.

SALLY: Thanks, Daddy.

JOHNNY and SPARKS: Thanks, Mr Grimshaw.

MR GRIMSHAW: That's all right, boys. Thank you. Come on everybody.

Exit all but GRIMSHAW, JOHNNY, SALLY, SPARKS *and* CARROTS.

MR GRIMSHAW: By the way, Salter.

JOHNNY: Yes, Mr Grimshaw?

MR GRIMSHAW: Maybe I was a bit hasty. Come to tea

next Saturday, and we'll see if you can't take Sally to the club that night.

JOHNNY: Crumbs, thanks!

Exit MR GRIMSHAW.

JOHNNY *turns to* SALLY *in amazement.*

JOHNNY: What's up with your Dad, then?

SALLY: He surprised me.

SPARKS: And me!

CARROTS: Maybe he's drunk or something. My Dad gets like that when he's had a drop too much.

SALLY: Can't be. I thought he'd be furious.

JOHNNY: Crumbs, but I've got to have tea with him again next Saturday.

SPARKS (*laughing in great glee*): So you have. Grandstand seat for me next time. Must see what you do next time.

CARROTS: Probably dunk him in your tea!

SALLY: Honest, he'll be all right now.

SPARKS: Wouldn't take any chances myself! (*He and* CARROTS *giggle together.*)

JOHNNY (*looking with a grin and a wink at* SALLY): Well now, that gives me an idea, Sally.

SALLY: Yes?

JOHNNY: Don't you think it would be nice to have Sparkler here, and Carrots to tea next week?

SPARKS: Hey! No. Anything – but not that!

SALLY: Do you know, Johnny, that's a wonderful idea! I'll talk to Mummy when they pick us up tonight, and fix it.

CARROTS: You wouldn't!

JOHNNY and SALLY: Wouldn't we?

SPARKS and CARROTS: Oh! No! You rotters!

SPARKS *and* CARROTS *collapse together on to a bale.* SALLY *and* JOHNNY *sit on the table together laughing heartily. The strains of* JOHNNY *singing 'If I ruled the World' slowly at first, then growing in pace and volume and joined by the accompanying piano has weaved through the last speeches. Now it swells out at full pitch and speed, as the* CURTAIN *closes on the four friends who are rolling in riotous laughter.*

THE END